Copyright © 2016 Edward Simpson and Alice Tilche

ISBN: 978-1-5262-0350-2

First Published in 2016 by School of Oriental & African Studies (SOAS).

A CIP catalogue record for this book is available from the British Library.

Funded by the Economic and Social Research Council ES/I02123X/1 UK and generously supported by the School of Oriental and African Studies, University of London.

Catalogue edited by Edward Simpson and Alice Tilche

Research, images and text provided by F.G. Bailey, Patricia Jeffery, Adrian Mayer, Daniela Neri, Tina Otten, Tommaso Sbriccoli, Edward Simpson and Alice Tilche.

Designed by Arianna Tilche

Printed by Pureprint Group

Typefaces
Relative 10 Pitch
Relative Book
Relative Book Italic

The future of the rural world?

The Future of the Rural World?

The future of the rural world?

Edward Simpson
and Alice Tilche

"The future of the rural world? India's villages 1950 – 2015" was an exhibition hosted by SOAS, University of London. The event marked the end of a major project funded by the UK's Economic and Social Research Council on 'restudying' village India.

Most of world's scholarly and media attention is on megacities and the story of rapid urbanisation they are held to represent. Slums have become photogenic and dramatic devices. However, the greater part of the world's population continues to live in rural areas. This will continue to be the case for some time to come. The consequential and untold story, however, is the radical transformation of the countryside, as things formerly thought of as villages become something else. These places mark the emergence of a new form of settlement which are neither cities nor villages in the conventional uses of such terms. The language of social science is ill-equipped for these new realities.

The aims of the original ESRC project had been straightforward: to conduct new fieldwork in villages where anthropological research had been undertaken in the 1950s in order to see what had changed.

Anthropologists who then made the voyage to India documented a sophisticated agrarian society ordered by caste and institutionalised inequality – where the division of labour mirrored the ritualised and hierarchical exchange relationships of caste. Today, their accounts form an unprecedented and intimate historical account of what life was like in villages during the heady years immediately after Independence.

The world has changed. In India, Nehru's socialism, strongly influenced by cold-war politics, has given way to the forces of (neo)liberalisation and globalisation. Waves of development policy have been unevenly implemented across the country; political devolution has passed some responsibility for economic development, social justice and taxation to the village level; affirmative

i

action ushered in caste-specific and gendered 'reservations'. Land-reforms and new technologies have transformed agriculture, whilst public health programmes enhanced children's chances of survival. Nehru's ghost has been exorcised by neoliberalism.

The original anthropological studies were undertaken independently by F.G. Bailey, Adrian C. Mayer and David F. Pocock (1928 – 2007). The three went on to have distinguished careers as exponents of the post-colonial sociology of India. The villages they studied are now located in the modern states of Odisha, Madhya Pradesh and Gujarat. All three locations display legacies of post-colonial development and political policies, consequences of economic and land reform or consolidation, and effects of technological and media expansion. In each location, there has been a clear growth of grassroots Hindu nationalist sentimentality, and a hardening of religious and ethnic lines. The salience of caste is less, but remains significant. Rural populations have grown between two and five times in size in the last sixty years.

What emerges most strongly from this project however is just how diverse rural futures are. The trajectories of three of India's 600,000 or so villages tell of quite divergent scenarios.

Going back further in time for a moment, the Indian village has played a surprisingly important role in global theories of history and politics, both conservative and revolutionary. Over the centuries, the village has been comprehensively used and abused, a site for fantasy of both the left and right, for liberals, mythologists and pundits. The idea has become a vessel into which all manner of political ambition has been poured. Maine, Marx, Engels and Weber all had something to say on the significance of rural life in India.

In the nineteenth century, Imperial arguments were made for economic liberalisation on the basis of customary inequalities and modes of property ownership reported in villages. For many radicals, in contrast, the village community exemplified qualities of life, such as liberty, equality and fraternity; all of which had been realised in some past époque or were realisable in some future utopia, but significantly, these qualities were currently at risk.

All in all, the village community occupied a painfully ambiguous position, symbolising the world European men had lost, a profoundly nostalgic view of an alternative society, which could be compared with the present for signs of both progress and degeneration.

The village remains on the brink of being lost forever, but it has been for at least two centuries, possibly longer. Village realities have changed, of course; but the way the village is situated as tangible but threatened remains. In the 1950s, it was quite clearly documented that the village was in the midst of radical change. Universal suffrage in 1950 was perhaps the single biggest event because suddenly villagers mattered to the politics of the nation in ways they had never done before.

At the time, Bailey, Mayer and Pocock saw that farming could no longer form the backbone of the village economy, new technologies, population pressure and the seep of the cash economy spelled the inevitable decline of agriculture. They also saw that there would be an increase in other forms of employment, and a corresponding shift in traditional patterns of hierarchy and inequality. The influence of land, at least on the scale of the village, was inevitably to lose ground to commercial acumen and cash wealth.

Since that time, remarkably similar conclusions have also been the repetitive key findings of six decades of rural studies, in India but also elsewhere. The countryside has been hollowed out, farming has ceased to provide an income for most, and dirty finger nails have gone out of fashion.

Today, in Odisha, land rights and tribal identities have become burning issues, as people have been brought into conflict with transnational corporations and rapacious extractive industries. However, the village remains recognisably as it was in the 1950s; those who survive from that time display more wrinkles for the camera, but their rituals and concerns remain similar.

Rapid industrialisation in Madhya Pradesh has brought villagers into wage relations with India's industrial houses. A new highway has sucked the core of the village out of the hinterland and closer to the tarmac and city. A surprising number of people who were not born in the village now live there, some of who have come from far away. A formerly impoverished Muslim population has become politically dominant.

In Gujarat, the village has become more firmly part of the transnational networks and nostalgic and nationalist politics of migrants in East Africa and UK. Violence in the state in 2002 saw minarets demolished, most Muslim residents subsequently decided they would be safer elsewhere. Life in these villages is clearly not the same as it was in the 1950s.

Some suggest the village has become a 'waiting room' for industrial labour markets; for others the village has withered, or even died. What has emerged has been described as an urban–rural continuum. Other neologisms (some of which are no longer that new) include, peri-urban, ex-urban, the fringe city, vicinities or vicinage, and hermaphroditic and in-between sprawl: the rurban!

The ESRC project allowed the luxury of looking and thinking backwards in time. The juxtapositions we came to face-to-face with encouraged us to identify trends and trajectories, and eventually brought us to our question: The future of the rural world?

The initial findings of our research once-again echo those already glossed from the literature: agriculture has crumbled, livelihoods have diversified, mobility, mass unemployment, 'over' education, and cultures of 'waiting' are endemic. Religion dominates public discourse in many locations. Land fragmentation is combined with speculative land and construction markets. Private monopolists dominate many local supply chains. Transnational capital has become increasingly sophisticated at extracting revenue. Service professions and a middle class have entered rural life. A mobility paradigm organises daily and life-cycle expectations for many.

However, instead of seeing these as catastrophes marking the end or degeneration or pollution of the world as we know it, our longitudinal perspective shows that these are in fact the ongoing processes at the heart of continuing to negotiate what it means to live in a village. To put it simply, these are the things of a village way of life, which have accelerated village modernities in different ways in the three sites.

Overall, the project suggested that city-dominated knowledge, the urban bias so naturalised in common thought and long-highlighted by scholars such as Michael Lipton, has turned rural India into a bloodstained battleground of planning and land deregulation, transecting and gated highways, developer bandits, windy electricity, fields of photolytic cells and mineral extraction. Today's paddy, is tomorrow's gated community or global township. Predatory capitalism and private monopolists run wild, as local economies are buoyed by speculative land investment and boom and bust spirals. The future looks rather grim, at least in some parts of what was once rural India.

v

The project has also suggested that the failure of the urban to absorb rural populations, and of the global to absorb the local, means that villages remain important places of identity and belonging, political mobilisation and welfare. The trajectories of the three villages we studied and restudied tell very different stories: in Odisha, surprisingly little has changed; in Madhya Pradesh, the countryside is 'rurbanising', as it is in Gujarat; there, however, we also see the village as a departure lounge. Many do well in America. Less is known about failure, return and reluctance, but these things may be the seeds of a new rural in India.

The future of the rural world?

Post-colonial India

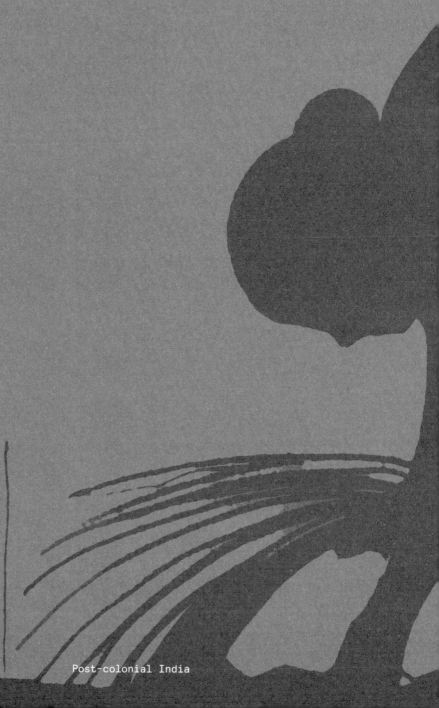

3

Post-colonial India

Some nineteenth century writers saw India as a living museum, which would allow them to understand the origins of European society.

For Karl Marx and Frederick Engels, the village in India was an early form of human development. In their view, the village had remained unchanged since the Dark Ages because there was no division of labour between villages.

All the trades and crafts necessary for the agricultural community to survive and reproduce were found within each village. Thus, there was no impetus for change or innovation because the village was a self-contained republic.

Such ideas remain remarkably commonplace today.

At Independence, India was dependent on food imports and nearly ninety percent of the new electorate lived in villages. Agriculture and villages were thrust centre stage in the politics of the country.

A rural 'uplift' exhibition was held in Delhi in 1946 under the slogan 'When agriculture stops everything stops'. Nehru vainly promised self-sufficiency by 1951. Floods, droughts and earthquakes hampered food production. Famine remained a danger, the politics of agriculture was quite literally a politics of life and death.

The Indian elections of 1951–1952 saw the use of the provocative slogan 'A vote for Congress is a vote for hunger'.

The Imperial Council of Agricultural Research described the task ahead as 'liquidating a vast and ancient rural slum'. Science and technology were generally seen as the way forward.

5

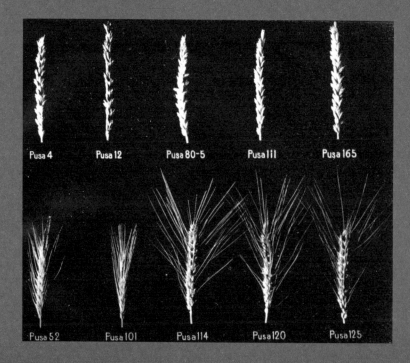

Pusa 4   Pusa 12   Pusa 80-5   Pusa 111   Pusa 165

Pusa 52   Pusa 101   Pusa 114   Pusa 120   Pusa 125

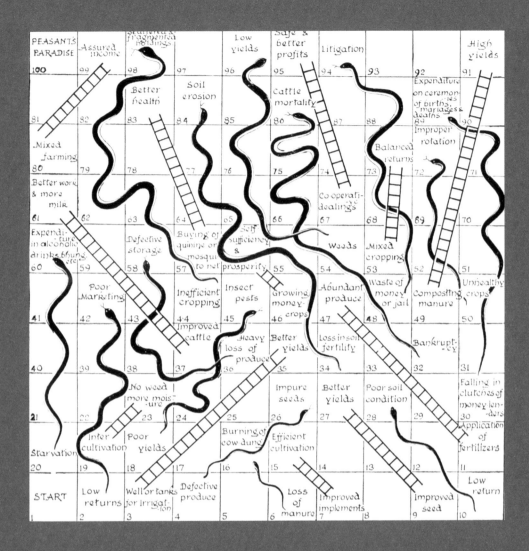

Farming propaganda
produced by the Imperial
Council of Agricultural
Research, 1946.

6

Independent India

7

Post-colonial India

Gandhi believed that self-reliant villages
were the foundation for a just, equitable
and non-violent order. He saw the future
of India in villages.

He initiated several model village projects,
notably at Champaran (Bihar, 1917) and
Sevagram (Maharashtra, 1920).

"If the villages perish, India will perish too.
It will be no more India. Her own mission in
the world will get lost".

"We are inheritors of a rural civilization.
The vastness of our country, the vastness
of the population, the situation and the
climate of the country have, in my opinion,
destined it for a rural civilization...To uproot
it and substitute for it an urban civilization
seems to me an impossibility".

8

Left:
Gandhi and other
figures witness the
great transformation,
Delhi, 1950s.

India was a British colony until 1947. The colonial government counted, measured and mapped the country. The 'village republic' emerged as a way of describing a village as a self-contained and self-governing unit and became one of the pillars of the Imperial ideology.

During the 1930s and 1940s, new ideas of development, modernisation and governance took root in India. At the time of Independence, there were divergent views on the best direction for the country.

Mahatma Gandhi saw the village as the future of a decentralised national government.

Dr B.R. Ambedkar thought village republics were the ruination of India. He asked: What is the village but a sink of localism, a den of ignorance, narrow-mindedness and communalism?

India's first Prime Minister, Jawaharlal Nehru, favoured industrialisation and believed that agricultural growth would naturally follow.

9

Right:
Poster art depicting
Nehru's vision for
an industrial India,
1950s, Bombay.

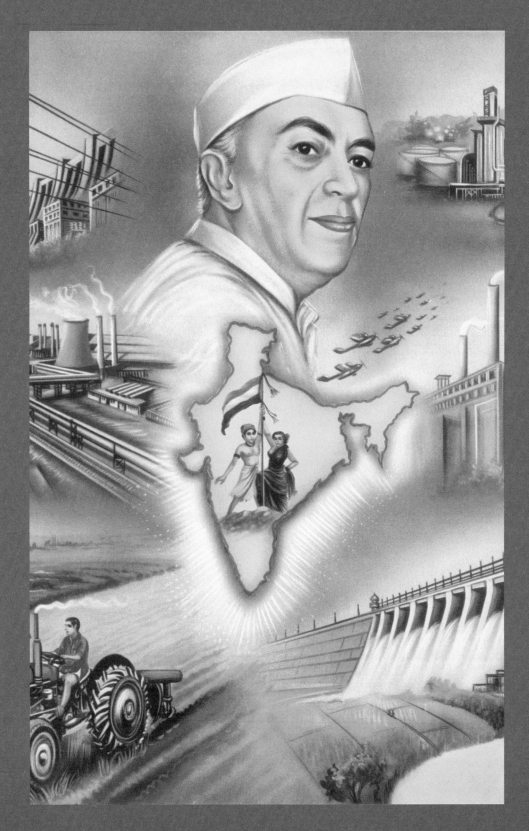

Moving into a technicolour world

11

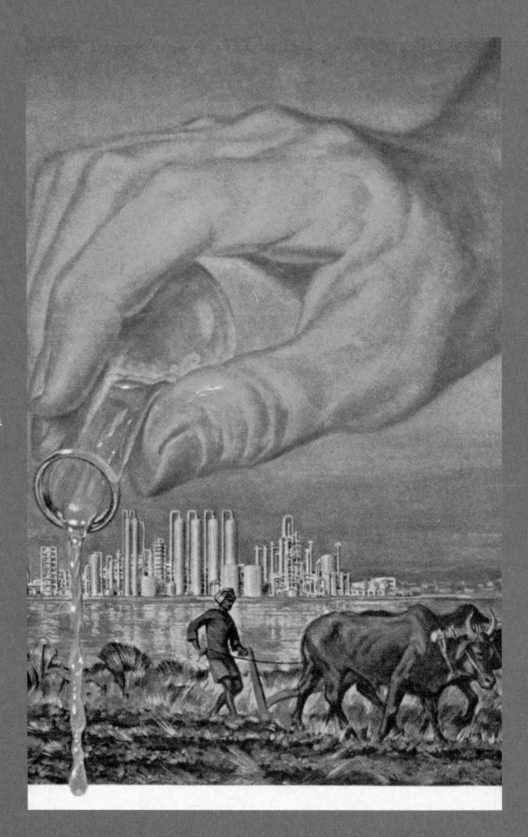

Post-colonial India

"Oxen working the fields…the eternal river Ganges…jewelled elephants on parade. Today these ancient symbols of India exist side by side with a new sight-modern Industry" so began the text of Union Carbide's advertising campaign, which was accompanied by the dual slogans "Science helps build a new India" and "A hand in things to come".

In 1984, the Union Carbide plant in Bhopal in Madhya Pradesh leaked methyl isocyanate into the atmosphere, killing many thousands of people.

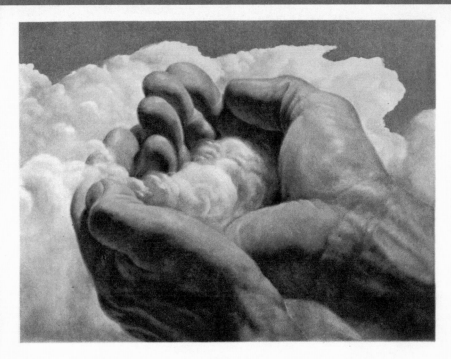
Moving into a technicolour world

Top:
The tractor, a symbol of modern farming, is fast replacing the old bullock-drawn plough in many parts of the country, State Bank of India, 1955.

Bottom:
Plentiful water! That's what a pump-set brings to the farmer. It scores over the age-old Persian wheel and other methods using animal or human muscle, State Bank of India, 1955.

Post-colonial India

Indian agriculture became a battleground for the superpowers of the Cold War. Foreign governments promoted rival cooperative and commercial agricultural models.

In the 1950s, food aid arrived under the slogan: 'Strength from America to the free world'. The Soviets opened a showroom for tractors in Bombay in 1955 and a model farm in Rajasthan.

In 1959, India hosted the first World Agricultural Fair. During the inaugural address, the American president Eisenhower spoke of how he planned to become a farmer when his present form of occupation came to an end. He spoke of "Food – Family – Friendship – Freedom".

14

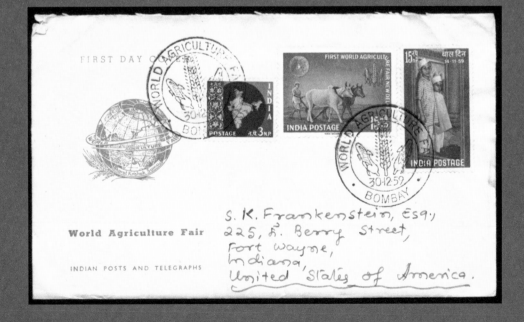

RAO BROTHERS,
TRIPLICANE.

JAI HIND

MS 318 D. P. Works, 2000 Copies, 25-9-47.

No. 8

16

Agricultural diplomacy

During the 1950s, a new wave of village studies conducted by Indian, American and British anthropologists began to appear. This was an era of science and confidence, when things were no longer simply black and white.

These studies involved intensive research in particular villages. The authors abandoned the evolutionary naturalism inspired by Marx and others.

These studies showed that the village was no longer an isolated unit, if indeed it ever had been. They conducted 'holistic' studies, investigating all aspects of village life.

Soviet T-75 tractors at the Sergo Ordzhonikidze tractor works in Kharkov, 1961.

17

Jamgod

Madhya Pradesh

The village of Jamgod in Madhya Bharat (now Madhya Pradesh) had a population of around 900 when Adrian Mayer (1922–) conducted fieldwork there for 15 months between 1954 and 1956. Mayer has continued to visit the village at intervals ever since, last visiting in 2013.

In addition to numerous articles and a rare longitudinal perspective, the research in Jamgod resulted in the influential book *Caste and kinship in central India* (1960).

In the 1950s, Jamgod was a mixed agricultural village dominated by the Kathi caste. Since then, the village population has expanded five-fold and livelihoods have diversified in parallel to the growth of a major industrial centre in the nearby town of Dewas.

Jamgod was 'restudied' as part of this research project by Tommaso Sbriccoli.

Towards Kankund

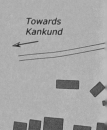

© Ballard (2016)

Jamgod - Old Village

N

0   30
metres

Towards the
Village

Shiv
Temple

Amba
Mata

Sitala
Mata

Temple
to Tejaji

Nag Maharaj Temple

Badrinath
Temple

Well

Private School

Public
School

PS

Dev Maharaj
Temple

PS

PS

Old Court
(Kacheri)

Mosque
& Darga

Besasu
Maharaj
Kumar
Temple

Hanuman
Mandir

Ram
Temple

Towards
Awalya Pipliya

It is 1950. The Second World War has recently ended, and three years ago India and Pakistan attained their independence.

In Britain, the post-war years also bring change. The NHS is established, and the universities are expanding. Social anthropology is drawing an increasing number of students. Some are undergraduates, but others have come to do research. Following the example of Bronislaw Malinowski, perhaps the most influential anthropologist of the inter-war years, they expect their research to be based on prolonged and exhaustive fieldwork.

In India, anthropologists have hitherto studied the so-called primitive (and usually preliterate) tribal populations. But, influenced by the new government's policy of rural development, these students have set their sights on the study of villagers – usually in a single village, since intensive fieldwork can best be carried out among a restricted population in which everyone is known to the researcher.

Against this backdrop, Adrian Mayer selected the following images from his considerable archive to represent life in Jamgod as he knew it circa 1954.

21

Jamgod

Adrian C. Mayer (left)
leaves Jamgod 1955

In 1954, Jamgod was
largely self-contained.
Though only a mile from
the highway between
the cities of Indore
and Bhopal, people
only went into the town
seven miles away if they
had business. A farmer
takes a cart with grain
to sell in the market
there. The journey
will take him about
six hours, there and
back. For those without
carts, there were two
buses per day each way
on the highway, but
these rarely stopped
at Jamgod, being full
long before they reached
the village.

Jamgod

Apart from business,
the reason to leave
the village was to
visit kin in other
villages linked to
Jamgod by marriage.
Such villages were
usually within range
of a day's journey by
bullock cart.
Here, a newly married
bride is taken on her
mother's brother's hip
to the waiting cart
which will take her to
her husband's village.

Within Jamgod houses
were almost all mud
walled and thatch
roofed. The larger
were divided into
rooms, the smaller
had two areas separated
by tall earthen grain
bins. The streets were
dirt, without gutters.
A carpenter is working,
surrounded by friends
who have stopped for
a smoke and a gossip.

Jamgod

Farming was done with
simple technology and
bullock power. A farmer
is sowing sorghum,
the basic foodstuff
(chapattis of wheat
were rare and more
expensive). He drives
the bullocks and his
wife drops the seeds
into a drill.

There was little
irrigation of the
village's land before
electrification in 1971.
In 1954, water was taken
from open wells with
leather buckets made
in the village and
drawn up by a pair of
bullocks. The area which
such a mechanism could
irrigate was small.

Women played a large
part in agriculture,
being only barred from
driving bullocks.
They helped with the
planting, the weeding,
and the harvest.
A woman winnows
sorghum at the family's
threshing place.

An Indian village - then and now

Most of the crafts
needed for agriculture
and everyday life could
be found within the
village. Each farmer had
a man of the carpenter
caste and one of the
blacksmith caste to tend
to his tools and cart.
These were hired on an
annual contract and paid
in kind at each harvest.
They also worked for
villagers' in house
building and so forth,
as the occasion arose.
The blacksmith works
at his simple forge.

Other services were
given to the villagers
by a series of
craftsmen of different
castes-the potter,
barber and others.
The leatherworker
repairs a pair of
slippers. They are
made of leather from
a villager's animal
and tanned in the
village. Factory
made shoes were rare,
since only the village
slippers were strong
enough to resist the
large thorns frequently
met in path or field.

Many payments in
the village were
not made with cash,
though cash entered
the village from
the sale of cotton
in the summer and
wheat in the winter,
and labourers might
work for cash wages.
Nevertheless, the two
small shops stocking
basic items conducted
three-quarters of their
trade with payments
in grain. Farmers paid
their artisans in kind
at each harvest, other
payments were made
for each job. A female
labourer receives
payment from the
grain harvest.

A Brahman priest
lived in the village.
He officiated at
village and family
rituals, for which
he was paid, also
being given alms
at customary times.
The drummer also
received alms for
his service at
village festivals
and processions.
A householder gives
alms to the drummer
on the day of the
full moon.

33 Many annual festivals
contained a procession
of villagers. Two of
the village's three
headmen (to left and
right in the front row)
lead the procession
on the last day of the
festival called Naumi
(Ninth) or Naudurga
(Nine Goddesses).
Behind them is a medium
(without headgear in the
second row) possessed by
a goddess. The procession
is taking wheatseedlings,
grown by the medium
during the nine days,
to be 'cooled' in a well.

Jamgod

The festival of
Holi centred on the
fire in which the
villagers believed
that the princess
Holika had been burnt
in punishment for
her worship of false
gods. The village
women, led by the
headmen's wives, have
returned from visits
of condolence to all
households who have
suffered bereavement
during the past year,
and are dousing the
fire with water.

35 On the occasion of
marriage, kinsfolk
came from as many other
villages as the hosts
had the means to invite.
Here, the kin related
to the father of the
bridegroom give him cash
presents. At his side a
note is taken, so that
the same (or greater)
amount can be returned
on a similar occasion.
Besides kin, any friendly
villager may also make
such a donation.

The kin on the mother's
side of the marriage
bring presents of
clothes. Since a girl
went to her husband's
house, and since
there was no marriage
within the village,
these presents were
always brought from
outside the village.
Their arrival showed
the geographic extent
of the marriage ties
stretching out
from Jamgod.

An Indian village - then and now

37 The feeding of guests
was a major expense
at weddings and
funerals, since not
only family but fellow
villagers could be
invited. Such feasts
took place in a field
or, as in this case,
on the street outside
the only large brick
and wooden building
in Jamgod. Since each
caste had its own
level of purity, the
line of guests is here
broken where members
are forbidden to eat
with each other. The
cook is however of a
pure enough caste to
be acceptable to all.

The government was
traditionally represented
by a hereditary headman,
there being three of
these in Jamgod's case.
Besides keeping law
and order with the
aid of two watchmen
the headmen collected
the tax on holdings of
land. The farmer (left)
hands over the money
to a headman (right).
Behind them other
farmers wait their turn.

39 Ownership of land was
    registered and entered
    into the record book of
    the village accountant.
    He was called on when
    there was a dispute over
    boundaries, the headmen
    being also present to
    keep the peace.
    The accountant consults
    his register, with one
    headman to his right and
    two to his left. Behind
    them stands a watchmen
    with his staff.

Jamgod

Soon after the
inauguration of the
Republic of India in
1950, it was decided
to democratise the
village administration
by introducing elected
village committeés.
The committee in Jamgod
holds a meeting.
At the centre is
an official of the
Cooperative Department
who is advising on
proceedings. To his
left sits the elected
chairman. Shortly after
this a hierarchy of
committees was started,
stretching up to the
district level. Jamgod
was represented on
some of these, and its
political boundaries
were widened.

This section of the exhibition is the fruit of a collaboration between the anthropologist Tommaso Sbriccoli and the photographer Daniela Neri.

"Our aim was to open up Adrian C. Mayer's visual archive of an Indian village towards the present and, in doing so, to engage with the ways in which anthropology represents 'others'."

In addition to his anthropology, Mayer was also a good photographer, and took hundreds of pictures of the village and its inhabitants. These images now form an invaluable archive of twentieth-century life in rural India.

When Tommaso and Daniela went to 'restudy' the village in 2012, Mayer's visual material became a key reference point for investigating contemporary ethnographic issues.

41

"Each section focuses on a particular theme and takes as its starting point one of Mayer's images to focus on the changing realities of daily life over time."

The images connect past and present through the reactivation of Mayer's archive and through the artifice of genealogical charts – one of the most important methodological tools utilised by anthropologists.

The contrasts between black and white and colour images, and between genealogical models and real family group pictures, are intended to make time appear ambiguous and to play with the distinction between technique, photographic technology and what is represented.

"The topics emerged from conversation and collaboration with people in the village. Together, these images, as a form of narration, are intended to place the passage of time in material form."

Particular family stories are shown on the second half of each panel. They are told in the style of photojournalism, creating a further rupture with traditional modes of anthropological representation.

Jamgod

Darapti is one of six children from a high caste
and prosperous family. According to Hindu customs,
upon marriage she should have gone and live
with her husband in his village. Instead, she lives
in Jamgod, where she has her own property,
buffalo and land, which she cultivates herself.

This arrangement is unusual in rural India, and her
story is one of emancipation within the limits of
often strict and gendered rules.

Darapti was married young, but quickly realised her
husband was blind. She returned home. Her father,
Pannalal, feeling cheated, agreed not to send her
back. He gave her some land and a house. She thus
started her own independent life, of which she is
extremely proud.

There are a few other women in the village who
have returned home after either divorce or the
death of their husbands. Such women live in their
brothers' houses; their post-marital status making
them inauspicious according to local beliefs.

Darapti's unusual circumstances make others in
the village circumspect. In some ways, she is seen
as 'acting as a man' because she runs a small farm
single-handedly. She also eats in her brother's
house, where she is served by her daughters-in-
law as if she were a man of the family. At the same
time, she cultivates her status as a married woman
through the careful selection of jewellery, clothes
and other symbols.

She does not know what happened of her spouse.
He could be dead.

At the time of her own death, the land and
possessions will be divided among her brothers.
She will only be able to decide the destiny of her
golden jewellery, which she bought for herself in
order to be both a proper wife and head of her
own family.

45

Jamgod

47

Jamgod

Darapti

Untimely deaths in rural India lead to potentially dangerous situations. The souls of those who die before the completion of their ideal lifecycle linger halfway between this world and the afterlife. They must be pacified and 'seated' through ritual means.

In Jamgod, this particular category of spirits is called paliya for men and parii maji (mother fairy) for women.

While many families in Jamgod have one parii maji, Hairwals, one of the lowest-status castes in the village, have many, which are embodied in stones. These are worshipped annually in a ritual called bhana barna.

The presence of these pari majis does not only tell of traditional religious practices, but points to unequal economic and power relations in the village. Most the stories relating to the pari majiis focus on accidents: the woman who fell into a well, was bitten by a snake or scorpion, or crushed on a building site. These are also stories of labour.

Since the 1950s many things have changed in the village in terms of caste relations. However, it is still the case that many poor women continue hard labour for low daily wages (around £1 per day as opposed to men's £1.50).

Women's bodies and gendered stones show change and continuity in Jamgod and visually connect death and inequality, labour and injustice.

51

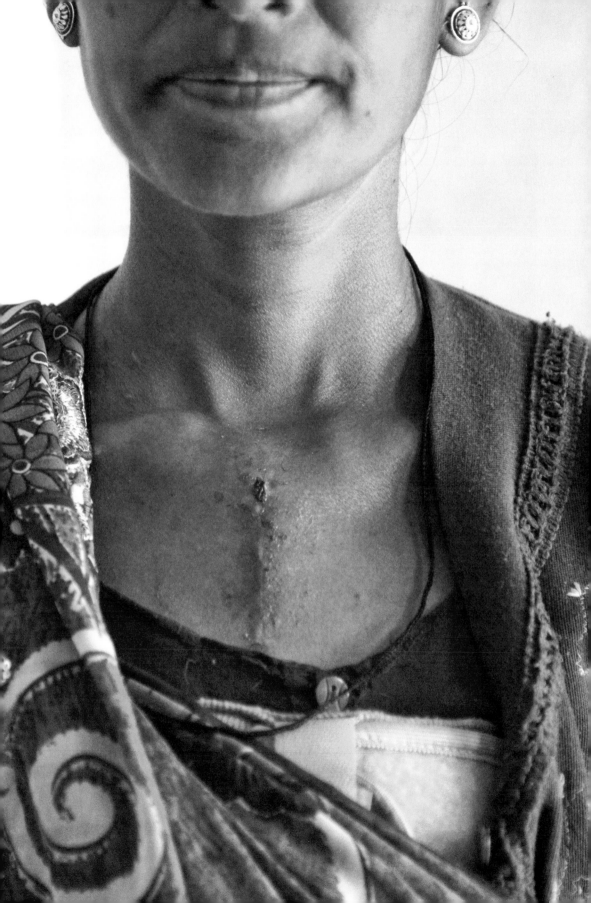

53

Jamgod

Pari Maji. Power, labour and death.

Bapudas belonged to the Harijan caste. He was an astrologer and performed rituals on collective occasions. His role as priest, even for lower castes, made him a respected source of advice in the village.

His youngest son, Charat, had run away from the village, abandoning his wife and children, to follow the popular guru Asaram Bapu.

Charat's wife had returned to Dewas, feeling that without a husband she was no longer welcome in her in-law's house. She opened a shop selling religious souvenirs near a temple in the town. With her profit, she rented an apartment and sent her children to a fee-paying school.

In 2013, things changed. Bapudas died and Charat, coincidentally, returned to the village after an absence of ten years. A few months later, Asaram Bapu, the guru, was arrested, accused of sexually assaulting a young girl. Charat has remained in Jamgod ever since, claiming his guru was framed. His wife struggles on in Dewas, bringing her children once a week to see their father in the village.

57

59

Jamgod

A religious tale

"A caste may be said to be 'dominant' when it preponderates numerically over the other castes, and when it also wields preponderant economic and political power. A large and powerful caste group can be more easily dominant if its position in the local caste hierarchy is not too low."

M.N. Srinivas, The social system of a Mysore village (1955).

A man was beheaded in Jamgod in the run up to the 1992 panchayat (village council) elections.

The executioner was from the Bhil caste, a numerous and rambunctious group who had made skilful political alliances with dominant groups to ensure their own economic and practical benefits.

The executed was the brother of Manghilal Yadav, who was standing for sarpanch (leader of the council) in the elections. His own Yadav caste, although small in number in the village, had strong links to criminal and political figures in the neighbouring town.

In the end, the beheading moved the villagers to support Mangilal, who won the election. His triumph ended a period of coalition between Khati and Bhil castes. Mangilal and his wife managed to rule the village for the next fifteen years, favouring his own Yadav community and harassing his opponents.

In 2008, a Khati boy publically reacted against Manghilal's harassment, which in turn triggered a feud, which eventually brought Yadav dominance to an end. The Khati caste, the largest community after Muslim Pinjaras, managed to elect their own sarpanch and behave much as Manghilal had done.

Manghilal is exiled from the village and many of those who supported him are in jail.

A shrine has been constructed where Manghilal's died, to mark an unfulfilled life. His wife regularly

63

visits. Manghilal, whose earthly power was aided by his
brother's spirit, dreams of a future revenge.

Politics is the capacity to dominate. This capacity is linked
to the size, strength and the ability to enact violence.
Most families in Jamgod own staffs, swords and some
even a gun. By the time they reach adolescence, many
boys will have received training in how to handle weapons.

Politics, dominance and violence

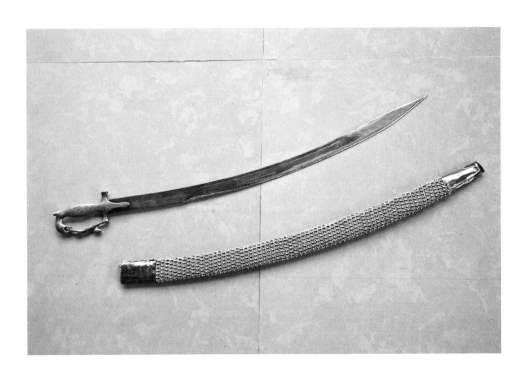

Politics, dominance and violence

Until quite recently, it was possible to see cows wandering the streets of India's largest cities. These animals have mostly been tidied up as part of urban modernisation and cleansing programmes. Cows are potent religious and political signs in India. For Hindus the animal is sacred and in many parts of the country it is forbidden slaughter cows and to eat beef. Cow dung and urine are believed to be purifying substances.

The dung or gobbar produced by cows, bulls and oxen continues to be important in village life.

Jamgod once had a cowherd, who was supported collectively by the village. This time has gone, as milk cows have been substituted by more productive buffaloes and cheaper goats.

Cow dung is collected to make both fertiliser and fuel. Dung mixed with mud and straw, shaped into thin cakes, or khanda, and left to dry on walls and floors makes an excellent fuel. In addition, government subsidies have encouraged the production of biogas from dung which is also used for cooking. Cow dung is also used as a building material.

Dung cakes are also important in many Hindu rituals, where they are used to cook bread balls, or batti, which are served at funerals and at other big family occasions. Dung is also used to create small figures utilised in the performance of many other rituals.

The first chapatti cooked at lunch and dinner is given to cows and at Diwali cows and oxen are decorated and worshipped. Oxen are still used to perform some agricultural activities, mostly by those without the means to buy or rent a tractor.

The village bull has no single owner and is revered and fed by all. He roams the village inseminating the cows who belong to those who cannot afford to pay for the services of a selectively-bred bull. The bull appears in most of village temples in

69

the form of Nandi, Shiva's mount. Gaumata (or
Kamadhenu) appears on the other side: the cow
in her divine form, believed to host in her body all
of the other gods.

The term godhul means sunset or cow dust, referring
to the dusky transition into evening, when the return
of the herd raises dust which lingers on still air.
The village settles into another night.

Guamata

Guamata

All but the 'untouchable'
castes depended on a
single well for their
drinking water. This
was fetched by wives
and daughters and
brought home in large
earthen or brass pots.
Note that one of these
women has covered her
face: this is because
she has married into
the village and should
behave modestly before
73   its men folk, Jamgod,
Madhya Pradesh, 1954.

Jamgod

Collecting water from a
tubewell, Jamgod, Madhya
Pradesh, 2012.

Then and now

Some 50 of the roughly
150 children of school
age attended the village
primary school-48 boys
and 2 girls. Most pupils
had dropped out by the
time of class 5, but
those who remained were
dutiful in doing their
homework wherever they
could, Jamgod, Madhya
Pradesh, 1950s.

Jamgod

Homework under the
electric light of the
family shop, Jamgod,
Madhya Pradesh, 2012.

77   The summer crops have
      been harvested, and
      now the ground must
      be prepared for the
      winter's cultivation.
      Under the clouds of
      the retreating monsoon,
      a farmer harrows his
      field, Jamgod, Madhya
      Pradesh, 1954.

Jamgod

A wealthy Khati family
scatters chemical
fertiliser by tractor.
The use of chemical
fertilisers is
widespread and has
almost completely
replaced natural
sources, Jamgod,
Madhya Pradesh, 2012.

Then and now

Sundarana, Gujarat

Alice Tilche

In the 1950s, the village of Sundarana had a
population of around 2,200 and was located in Kaira
District of the Bombay State. The village was studied
by the anthropologist David F. Pocock (1928 – 2007),
who spent eighteen months there between 1953
and 1956. Then it was a mixed agricultural village,
dominated by the Patidar caste.

Pocock wrote two books about Sundarana: Kanbi
and Patidar (1972) and Mind, body and wealth (1973).
The first is a treatise on caste, kinship and marriage;
the second is a consideration of the changing
nature of popular Hinduism in the region.

Since then, the village population has doubled and
is now part of the modern Gujarat State. The Patidar
or Patels continue to dominate the affairs of the
village, although today international migration is
more important to the village than agriculture.

Sundarana was recently revisited by Alice Tilche,
who spent twelve months there as part of this
research project.

Sundarana Village

To
Village High School,
Shiv Temple & Petlad

Sundarana
Lake

Temple complex

Mosque

Chok

Dairy
co-operative

Dove
cot

Vankar
Vas

Thakivanu
Phallyu

Prajapati
Vas

Chok

Vallabh
Chok

Subash
Chok

Sayoghi
Karki

Brhampol

Navi
Karki

Vanduvran
Chok

Umar
Vago

Girdarnagar

Sobhrat
Vago

Nava
Avaz

Vaghrivas

Indira
Colony

New Patel
Society

Indira Colony

To
SH 5 &
Borsad

To
Shankalpura

N

0   50
metres

સ્વ.શારદાબેન ગિરધરભાઈ ના સ્મ્

Village entrance gate,
Sundarana

Sedentary life is often seen as the natural starting point of human civilisation. But is it? In India, various empires and the modern state have tried to sedentarise populations, as an effort to extract tax revenue and to control their subjects. Many of those who were encouraged to settle have again become migrants as their ways of life, to do with agriculture for example, are no longer sustainable or desirable.

People inhabit villages in different ways. Sundarana is a village of 4,842 people. There are around 40 different Hindu, Muslim and Christian communities. Some live in concentrated and some in scattered settings. There are those who live on the fields they farm and those who travel to them; there are pastoralists who pass by the village and pastoralists who have made the village their home.

There are migrants of various kinds: those who commute out of the village everyday to labour in factories or in fields further away; others travel to be teachers, clerks and shopkeepers in adjacent towns. There are those who migrate to other regions of India, working as traders, shopkeepers, business people, cleaners and factory workers.

There are those who migrate abroad as students or as tourists in the hope that they will be able to stay. Some come back after their degrees and visas run out, while others stay on. There are those who established themselves overseas, where they now have businesses and families. Some have built houses back in the village and return every few years. Women often migrate to marry, moving away from their natal places to their husband's village or new country of residence.

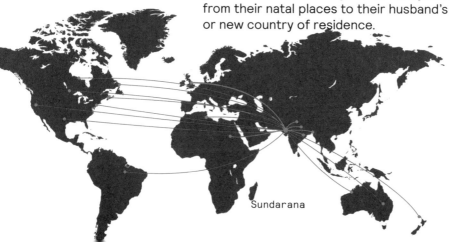

Sundarana

According to the World Bank, recorded remittances
from migrants to their countries of origin reached
$440 billion in 2015.

India is the leading recipient of remittances,
receiving $70 billion in 2014. The state of Gujarat
contributes significantly to this figure.

Remittances are not just cash transfers,
although they most commonly take this form.
Remittances can also be a form of investment
in business, construction or land. Half of the
recorded philanthropic donations go directly
to religious trusts and organisations.

In some villages, remittances are far higher than the
amount invested by the state into village development.

Remittances boost local economic growth, but are
usually directed at specific families, communities
and organisations with the effect of widening
inequalities between migrants and non-migrants.

84

85

Devotees gather
outside the BAPS
Swaminarayan Temple in
Bochasan, a village
neighbouring Sundarana.
BAPS is a powerful
and international
religious congregation,
importantly funded
by the donations of
Non Resident Indians.

Drawing by
George St Clair.

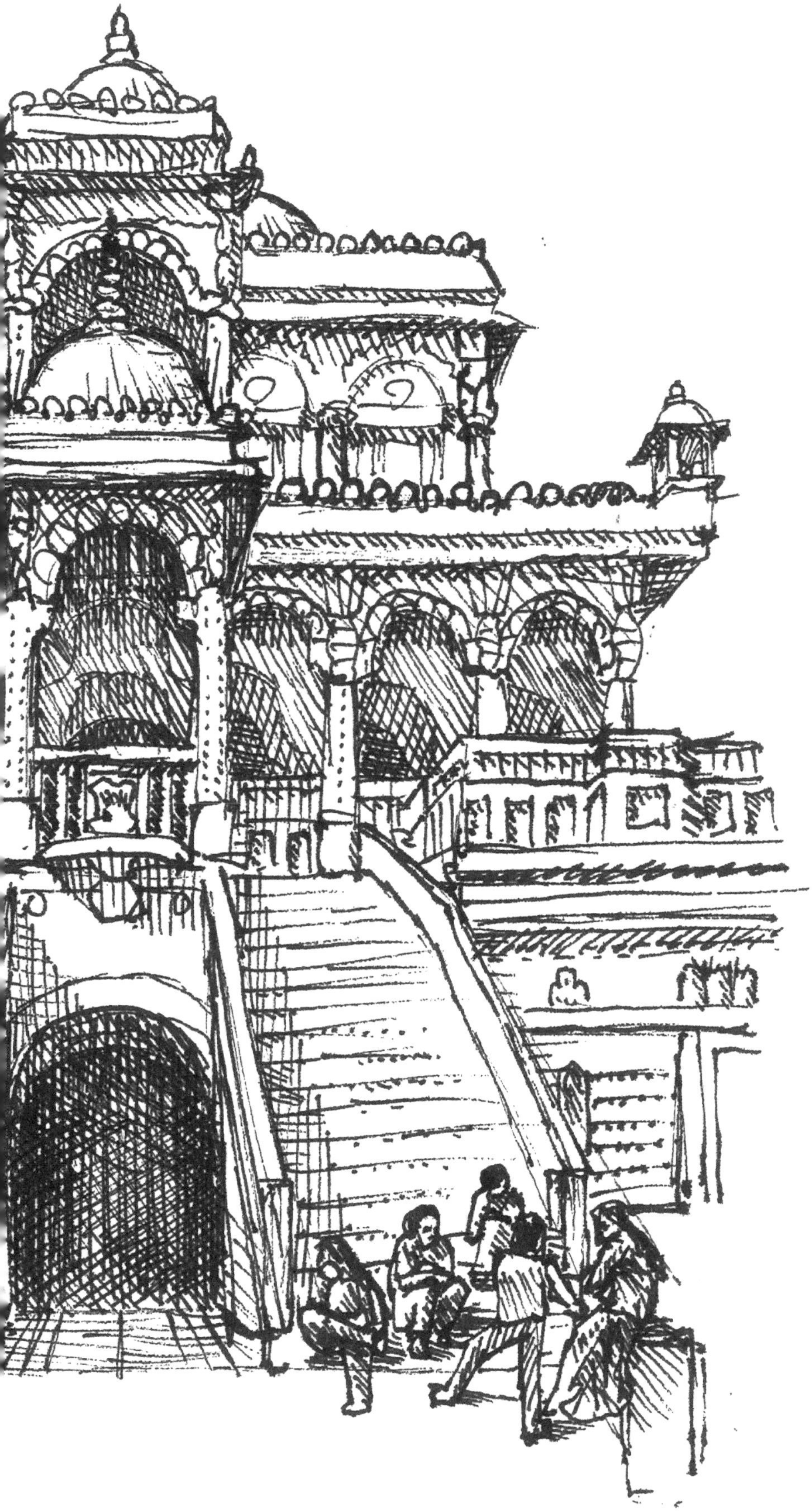

86

Shrine to Kalimata.
The priest of this
Goddess is well known
in Sundarana as
'the guru who gives
visas'. Young aspiring
migrants consult the
Goddess with their
visa applications
and passports to
receive blessings.

Bank of Baroda: one of
13 banks in the richer
village of Dharmaj,
neighbouring Sundarana.

Money

89

Migrant family to Kenya
and the United Kingdom
build a new house at
the village outskirts.

From cultivation
to construction:
agricultural land
for sale in a small
town near Sundarana.

Timepass: the action or fact of passing the time, typically in an aimless or unproductive way.

Timepass in Sundarana is a common past-time among educated and unemployed young men. Many men in the village have graduate and post-graduate qualifications. They aspire to get good jobs and eventually migrate overseas.

However, most of these aspirations do not become realities. Many men end up working on their family's land and supervising the work of other farm labourers.

Among the Patidar community, farmers are considered poor, as international migration has become the preeminent marker of status and success. Young farmers find it difficult to build new houses, to get loans for long term investments and, most of all, to find brides. Women do not want to marry farmers.

91

Young under-employed and unmarried men spend a lot of their time riding around on motorbikes, drinking tea, flicking through their mobile phone and sitting together at crossroads.

Waiting, some say, is a common feature of societies that have been incited to believe in a future that they cannot achieve.

Young men hang out near
the village entrance.

'Timepass' and masculinity

93

Samirbhai and his
scooter. At the time
of this drawing in 2012,
Samir had just returned
from London after his
student-visa expired.
He was waiting for
a new visa to Canada.

Drawing by
George St Clair.

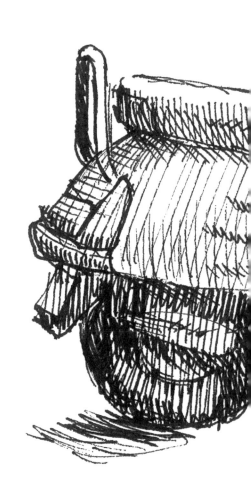

95

Deepwali 2012: young
men from the Thakor
community sit around
and show off their
new clothes.

Deepwali 2012: young
men from the Patidar
community hang out
at their usual meeting
point and pose with
new clothes.

'Timepass' and masculinity

Wedding celebrations:
a USA citizen (standing
girl) returns for a
visit to the village
and attends the
wedding of a relative
(sitting girl).

At birth, there should be 104 – 106 males to every 100 females. In India and Vietnam, the figure is around 112 males for every 100 females. In China, it is almost 120 to 100. The problem of India's missing girls is most prominent in its north-western regions. Practices more prevalent in the past, such as infanticide and the neglect of baby girls, continue with modern technology such as sonography and sex-selective abortion.

The sex ratio for children between 0 and 6 years of age around Sundarana is 877 females to 1,000 males, against an anticipated 950:1,000. In an attempt to stop sex-selection abortions, it has become illegal to reveal the sex of an unborn baby.

Young women complained that 'there are too many boys in the village!'.

Young men complained that women had become 'too cool' for them. Many young girls were the first in their family to be educated to university level. They put considerable effort into their studies, often outperforming men.

Women wished most strongly to leave behind peasant life. They also aspired to break from tight-knit family relations and the domestic duties they would have to perform for their in-laws. No woman in Sundarana wanted to marry a farmer. Instead, women aspired to marry migrants, so as to be able to leave the village. Some succeeded. Abroad, the reality was often different to what they had imagined.

99

Girls hang out near
the village entrance
after voting in the
regional elections.

High school girls sing
the national anthem
during independence day.

Girl power?

Agriculture is stagnating throughout India and unable to absorb a growing rural population. Common trends include the fragmentation of landholdings, the decline in workers that list agriculture as their main occupation and the growth of so-called 'rural non-farm employment'.

Sundarana is located within a fertile plain, known locally as the 'garden of India'. From the perspective of other rural places, the region is rich.

Patidars form less than twenty percent of the village population but own more than eighty percent of the land. Most Patidars are landowners, while other communities work on Patidar lands.

During the colonial period, this community became favoured as primary cultivators and were charged with collecting land revenue. During the 1800s, they benefited from the introduction of the railways, new irrigation schemes and cash crops such as tobacco. They were also the main beneficiaries of the green revolution. Today, chilli has become the main cash crop as the tobacco industry is in decline.

While agriculture continues to be productive, it is no longer considered a profitable or dignified occupation. Farmers are considered poor.

Young Patidars aim to leave their farming estates behind. Those who till land also aim to leave for more remunerative jobs in factories and cities, and in order to escape old and exploitative relations of patronage.

Women are those who mostly continue working in agriculture, alongside labourers who migrate from poorer areas of the country.

101

Advertising for
IPCO creamy snuff:
a tobacco paste for
oral use manufactured
in the region.

103

Daily wage labourers
bundle dry tobacco
leaves.

Drawing by
George St. Clair.

104

105

Agricultural labourer
transplanting ripened
tobacco leaves.

Tobacco crop
in Sundarana.

Agriculture
Tobacco

109

Daily wage labourers
bundle dry tobacco
leaves.

Tobacco farm and factory
owner displays a stack
of dry tobacco leaves.

Agriculture
Tobacco

Chilli

111

Sundarana

112

Agricultural daily
wage labourers plant
chilli seeds.

115

Candle lit for
auspiciousness
at the entrance
of the field.

Agricultural daily
wage labourers plant
chilli seeds.

Drawing by
George St Clair.

Women take rest before transplanting chilli plants to a bigger field. The field is flooded beforehand so that the young plants will go in easily. The work is strenuous and women have to stand for hours bending over, with mud to their knees.

119

Chilli plants ripen
to be transplanted to
a bigger field.

Middlemen weigh,
trade and buy chillies
that will be sold to
neighbouring regions.

Falling birth rates and increasing life expectancy means the population is ageing rapidly. In 2011, there were over 100 million people in India over the age of 60, a number which will almost double by 2025.

8 out of 10 elderly people live in rural areas.

In the traditional joint-family, the elderly would be cared for by their children. In this area of India, which is both patri-lineal and patri-local, women mostly move after marriage to their husband's village and family. Caring for their husband's ageing parents is part of women's work, while a women's own parents will typically be cared for by her brother's wife. This logic also promotes the desirability of sons over daughters.

Joint families are increasingly breaking up. The reasons are many: the rise of individual values and aspirations, rivalries between brothers, land fragmentation and the decline of agriculture, the pursuit of education and jobs, and migration.

122

Chanchanben, a widowed
mother of six daughters,
lived alone.
She belonged to a rich
family but all her wealth
had gone into marrying
her daughters well.

125

Ramanbhai, Chetnaben,
Satnaben and Keribhai
also lived alone.
Their sons migrated
to East Africa and the
United States. Their
daughters had married
away from the village.

Sundarana

Ageing

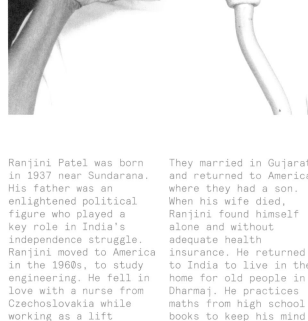

Ranjini Patel was born in 1937 near Sundarana. His father was an enlightened political figure who played a key role in India's independence struggle. Ranjini moved to America in the 1960s, to study engineering. He fell in love with a nurse from Czechoslovakia while working as a lift operator in a hotel in the 'love city' of San Francisco.

They married in Gujarat and returned to America, where they had a son. When his wife died, Ranjini found himself alone and without adequate health insurance. He returned to India to live in the home for old people in Dharmaj. He practices maths from high school books to keep his mind active. He wants to return to America.

Old friends in the
home for old people
in Dharmaj.

Bisipada: Odisha

Tina Otten and
F.G. Bailey

F.G. Bailey (1924–) conducted fieldwork in Bisipara (then population 700) and smaller 'Baderi' (properly Boida) in the Kondmahal District of Orissa between 1952 and 1955 and again in 1959.

He wrote three books based on this research (1957, 1960, 1963) which describe and analyse social change at the level of the village, caste and regional politics. He was particularly interested in the effects of universal suffrage and new forms of economy on village life.

Bailey later revisited his Bisipara research with three retrospective monographs. These are sublime and gloomy accounts, written to establish the philosophical and moral underpinnings of daily life in the village in the 1950s.

Tina Otten went to conduct new fieldwork in what is now called Bisipada, in Kandhamal District of Odisha. As with the other researchers on this project, she explored Bailey's hypotheses, attempted to gauge what had changed in the intervening six decades, and asked new questions befitting of a new era in India.

Towards
Dehurisahi

Towards
Padiaberna
& Katniapada

Hatapada

**Disused weavers'
house**

Kumbharsahi

**House of the
priest of the
earth**

**Old
dispensary**

Podasahi

**Thakurani gudi
(small shrine)**

Towards
Bhaliapad

Badala Berna

nda
rna

Trinath
temple

Mati
Debata

Meeting
house
Kumbharsahi

Meriah
tree ★

Meriah
bush ★

Sundisahi

**PDS
centre**

**Panchayat
Building**

**New Ram
Temple**

Sabarnasahi

**Meeting
house**

**Bisipada Pond
haratiya Bandha**

Jori Chuan

Gumsuriasahi

Post
Office

Boraldevi
temple

**House of former
sardar (headman)**

Chabrikuti Berna

Anganwadi
centre

**Shiva Temple
(Kandhamal
temple)**

**Inspection
bungalow**

**Disused
police
outpost**

**Revenue
Inspectors
office**

Towards
Dangakhol

Stockman
Centre

**Primary
Health
Centre**

Doctors' Quarters

Mandiapadar

**Forest Office
Building**

Old disused granary

Kadalasahi / Harisahi

**Kambeshwari
Temple**

N

**Cremation
Ground**

150

netres

d Bisipada Village

Dangakhol

Subarna Street, which F.G. Bailey called Warrior Street. It remains the social cultural centre of the village, where most annual festivals take place. In the late afternoon people return from the fields or from work in the nearby town. Girls hurry to start cooking dinner. The old lady sitting in the blue house right is the wife of Mr Debohari Bisoi, F.G. Bailey's former assistant in the field.

133

The Salunki river
in the 1950s, as
F.G. Bailey saw it.
The lines of stones
in the front and the
middle ground are
recognisable today.

The River

Bisipada is situated in the Kandhamals hilly and
forested areas. Terraced fields, rivers and brooks
are home to the Kandhamal tribes and their clients,
the Pana. The story goes that the Hindu communities
migrated from the plains to the West and into the
region around three centuries ago. Even today,
the journey from the plains – from Baudh and via
the district capital of Phulabani – involves crossing
the Salunki River in order to reach the village.

Bisipada

The Salunki river as
seen from the highway   134
bridge, Bisipada 2012.

Social and economic infrastructure
The river

135

Health

The medical facilities of the state continue to
compete with local medicinal practices. Various
health programs have been launched in the district,
the most recent is a health insurance scheme for
farmers. According to the statistics of the local
health centre, all childbirth takes place in hospital.
Local hospitals in Phulbani are called upon for minor
illness. More serious complaints might warrant the
five hour journey to Berhampur or even a trip to
the neighbouring state of Andhra Pradesh.

Education

The state provides health and education services and
different programs for some of the poorer citizens.

136

One of the two bicycle
shops, Mr Gobindo Bisoi,
Bisipada, 2012.

Economy

The commercial centre of Bisipada is called Hatapoda or Market Street. The families of the former distillers or the Ganjam and Boudh groups shop here. Today, Bisipada has a number of tailors, bicycle shops, a flour mill, a few 'fast food' outlets and a number of grocery stores.

An established grocer on Market Street, Bisipada, Mrs S. Sahu, 2012.

138

The sarpanch
Balakrushna
Kohoro (centre)
and other members
of the panchayat,
Bisipada, 2012.

Political

A sarpanch is usually the elected head of a village-level statutory institution of local self government called the panchayat or village council.

140

Khirod Sahani sarpanch
(1997-2002), Bisipada,
2012.

Shiva temple, the site
where the Scheduled
Caste community had
asked for entry after
the temple Entry
Act was passed (see
film *The Civility
of indifference*),
Bisipada, circa 1953.

Religion

At the time of F. G. Bailey's research, the Mali
family were servants of the Brahmin priests of the
Shiva temple. In the 1950s the Scheduled Caste
community was prohibited to enter the temple,
now they are important members of the temple
trust, Bisipada, 2012.

Shiva temple with
priests from the
Mali community,
Mr Nandkishore and
Promod Mahapatra,
daughter and
Mr Mahendra Bisoi.

The civility of indifference

Based on an original
work by F.G. Bailey.

Clockwise: Laxshmi,
Nila, Myra and John,
Bisipara, circa 1953.

The British left India in 1947. Children of freedom
were nursed through the Partition of the country.
Hindus, Muslims and Sikhs wounded and killed each
other in the largest movement of people in history.
The story usually goes that violence and religion
have been conjoined in the national imagination
ever since.

Let me lecture you for a moment: no serious student
of violence considers it to be 'natural' or 'primordial'.
Violence might be born of poverty, rivalry, or being
misunderstood – but these conditions on their own
do not lead to the wounding or death of others.
It takes something else to make people cross that
line, for civility to become incivility, and indifference
to become the passion for which one would wound.
But what does it take?

What prevents you from killing?

Bisipada

Please do not shrug off my question. It is a good question and awkward. I ask again, what stops you?

I imagine this question runs against ideas so deeply held that you do not readily know what they are.

The story you are about to hear is my attempt at answering these questions. I will use the tools of social anthropology and explain what I am doing as I go along.

I will take you below the big events of history and into the daily life of eastern India, at least as I knew things to be when I stayed there. I, along with my wife and children, lived in a village called Bisipara. Population 700. It is 1953, a very long time ago, another world almost.

The tale is about the powerful and unspoken ideas that kept people from killing each other: violence that never was. It was just a few years after Partition, but there was no tangible trace of it in villages such as Bisipada.

Anthropologists often study invisible things called social relations. They do so in the belief that how we relate to one another, can help explain who we are and what values we hold.

My story is also about threats.
For anthropologists, making a threat is a form of social relation. Threats suggest possibilities and futures. Threats live on in the exchange of a glance or a sack of rice. Threats, especially of violence, can make new worlds become real.

My big question then is: why were the people of Bisipara not genocidal enthusiasts?

Bisipara people were 'normal', for want of a more humane word, with the usual complement of good and evil, more tolerance than bigotry. Had they been able to imagine genocide, they would have judged it a disastrous indulgence, a stupidity, and a way to destroy themselves. Moderation and chaos, as clear alternatives, were never articulated.

145

What I am claiming of the Bisiparans is my own take on them as an anthropologist, a summation of all they told me, all I saw, as well as of all that they did not explicitly tell me and tried to keep from me. The rule that required them to show self-restraint was, so to speak, subliminal, part of their collective consciousness but unspoken, and apparent to me – more now than then – only in the way they conducted themselves.

Ritualised politeness shaped their public discourse; they displayed careful attention to the etiquette of status. Sometimes they slipped, and tempers showed. Bystanders indicated this was bad form. However, they were not all equal. Far from it, they had a system called caste, in which people were hierarchically ordered and substantially different at different levels of order. For them, humans were not all the same. They also had people who ranked lower than the castes, they thought of these people as 'untouchable', too polluting to be touched.

Untouchables had their own wells, residential
quarters and ways of doing things, quite separate
from those of caste Hindus.
In 1949, the government of the region, and in
accordance with Gandhi's wishes, passed an
act making it an offence to bar untouchables
from temples. Significantly, the act implied that
untouchables are in no essential way different
from other people. In places like Bisipara, this
was a radical new idea.

The Untouchables of Bisipada, Dalits they would be
called now, were known as the Panos. They made a
bid to enforce the act in the village, a protest against
customary discrimination. The occasion was a major
festival probably the celebration of the deity's
birthday. The Untouchables arrived all together,
as they did every year, attended by musicians, and
demanded they be allowed to enter the temple.

This confrontation was done in a manner that had
become the approved political style in India. Notice
of confrontation was given to those likely to oppose
the move. The response of the caste Hindus was
to mount a guard of men armed with battle-axes
around the temple.

But the Panos had taken a further step and informed
the local authorities. The result was the unhurried
arrival in the village of the local equivalent of a riot
squad consisting of a subinspector and two police
constables on bicycles.

The Hindus did not directly dispute the law, but said
that they were merely the trustees of the temple,
not its owners, and while they themselves would
stand down and permit the Panos to go inside,
they could not in good conscience do so without
consulting all the other Hindus, for, as everyone
knew, the temple in question belonged, not to the
village of Bisipara, but to the region.

The Panos stepped down and staged no more
confrontations. That was the time they built a
temple in their own street.

The clean castes punished the Panos for their
display of power by taking away the privilege of

making music on festive occasions. Thus, in this symbolic fashion, the clean castes signified that they no longer considered Untouchables a legitimate part of the community.

Perhaps that interpretation is too extreme. Panos, unquestionably, were of a different essence, a different moral fiber. So was every caste different from every other caste. Nevertheless, despite this perfectly racist sentiment, and despite the troubles at that time, there was a strong underlying sense (vague but quite perceptible) that being part of a community was something given, always there, inescapable, a moral inevitability.

Why did a foray not escalate as it may have done elsewhere? The main answer, was that all of those concerned, were accustomed to counting the cost. This habit of mind inhibits moral fervor. A resolute pragmatism, together with a pervasive suspicion that opportunism is everywhere, make it hard to be a true believer, for whatever cause. But what I witnessed was part of a revolution in which the old orders of power were beginning to be swept away. This shift was very much in Bisipara's public domain; the caste Hindus talked about it frequently and heatedly.

They did not take more resolute collective action. They often seemed more like actors in a play than people for whom real power was at stake. They were card players who never cashed in their chips, not because they wanted to prolong that particular game but because everyone knew that to convert the game into reality would hurt them all.

No one was a habitual gormandizer; they did not admire hard physical work. Life was not easy. But they were patient, generally phlegmatic, living mostly from day to day.

They were calculators and pragmatists, firmly in the habit of working out consequences when they made decisions. They did not theorize. Nor did they entertain themselves by imagining alternative lifestyles or contemplating reforms. They did not question – at least not of their own accord – their customary ways and the shape of their society.

I could not imagine them willing to die (or to kill)
for a principle or a cause.

The quarrel in Bisipara was less over material
resources than about human dignity, about getting
people to acknowledge, publicly, who had control.
In this context, to be legitimate means to be accorded
dignity, to be recognized as a person having specific
rights. One can have power without having legitimacy.
In Bisipara, legitimacy was by no means a pearl beyond
price. The cultural performances that I saw – the
political theatre of a struggle for power between
untouchables and clean castes – were carefully
staged and insulated so that there would be no
damaging fallout on a style of life so internalised in
the village.

What I have described are the foundations of social
relations in Bisipara: their definition of how the world
really worked – something that they all agreed and
acted upon, and therefore found to be authentic.

I began to write this memoir of Bisipara's dip toward
incivility in the 1990s, some forty years after I had left
that place for ever. My concern was to memorialise
those people as I saw them in those hopeful and
promising years, when the world was no longer at
war and decolonization was forging new times.

I later learned, that this century had brought terrible
mass violence to the region. It meant that the first
dip in civility I witnessed in the 1950s had gained the
momentum of a full-blown plummet.

In 2008, all around Bisipara Hindus and indigenous
people killed Christians, sometimes in horrific ways.
What made the killers believe they had the right to
do so? What made them put aside their indifference?

If we follow my original line, then these people
no longer counted the cost – or, perhaps more
accurately, they calculated the rules of the game
had changed – they were playing cards for a different
sense of community, the kind formed by the sentiments
of religious and political chauvinism, rather than by the
survival of a divided village community.

The rise of Hindu nationalism and institutionalised differentiation on the basis of religious and caste lines is the story in the villages of post-colonial India. Hindu organisations worked hard, and systematically, to reclaim the history of the country and to claim national political space for themselves. In India today, violence has become a political resource and is regularly ignited, like fire, in the run-up to elections, creating communities of fear and votes. In villages across the country, the rules of the game really have changed since the 1950s, when things appeared black and white, we see now the indifference of a new civility.

The civility of
indifference (2015)

Length: 15 minutes

This experimental film
is based on an original
work by F.G. Bailey of
the same name.

The narrator charts the
rise of aggression in
the highlands of Orissa.
The accompanying images
explore the power of
agrarian and sacrificial
metaphors in rural life,
and what it means to
witness something.

Director:
Edward Simpson

Research & co-direction:
Tina Otten & Sunny Suna

Narration:
Indira Varma

Editing:
William Elliott-Mills

The civility of indifference

Levelling. In the
background women are
transplanting rice
seedlings from a nursery
to a wet rice field,
Bisipada, 1953.

Ploughing and levelling

Bisipada is a rice-producing village, but the quality
of the soil and the climate permits only one harvest.
Wet rice is produced with a water irrigation system
on terraced fields.

Ploughing. In the
background women
are transplanting
rice seedlings
from a nursery to
a wet rice field,
Bisipada, 2013.

Planting

In the 1950s the
seedlings were planted
in rows. This method was
abandoned a few decades
ago. Today, women plant
the seedlings in circles
around themselves,
Bisipada, 2012.

Working in the wet rice
fields, Bisipada, 1953.   154

Agricultural cycle
Planting

Harvesting

Paddy is laid out in
the fields for 1-3 days
to dry, Bisipada, 2012.

Husking paddy with
a wind machine,
Bisipada, 2013.

Agricultural cycle
Harvesting

Dried mango, paste,
chutney and powder
from the kernels are
produced in nearly every
household during the
season, here shown by
family Mr Sukhandeba
Behera, Bisipada, 2013.

Agricultural byproducts

Mango and other seasonal products from the
kitchen garden and the forest complement the
routine diet and may sometimes be sold for cash.

Mrs Piro Bisoi
shows different
stages of mango
kernels, Bisipada, 2013.

Agricultural cycle
Agricultural byproducts

159 Mr Jayadev and Mrs
Shakuntala Bisoi after
the wedding ceremony,
Bisipada, 1953.

Weddings

The couple,
Bisipada, 2013.

End of body

The last home of the
soul of the deceased
is a clay pot at the
crossroads on the way
to the cremation ground.
Food is offered at
night to the soul.
The first insect
eating the offering
will be captured and
taken to the family
altar of the deceased.
The insect serves as
a vehicle to carry the
soul of the deceased
back to the family home.
Bisipada, 2013.

Elaborate day-long
rituals lead the soul
of the deceased into
the realm of the dead.
Sons mourn the death
of their mother. Her
husband is not present
during the ritual. As
a widower, his ritual
status has decreased
and his eldest son takes
over the role as head
of the household with
all its ritual duties,
Bisipada, 2013.

The last day of Lanka
Podi, Bisipada, 1950s.

Lanka Podi

The two month long performance of Lanka Podi
is a variation of the Ram Lila. It is a dramatic
reenactment of the life of Rama, ending up in
a ten day battle between Rama and Ravana,
as described in the Hindu religious epic of the
Ramayana. The event attracts visitors from
across the state. Recently the performers have
been invited to perform parts of the play in the
capital in Bhubhaneshwar.

Right:
Dancers and masks at
dawn at the final day,
Bisipada, 2013.

At the roots of a huge tree near to the house of the priest of the earth, the hands of the last meriah are buried. At this spot, women are blessed as part of the ritual. Priest of the earth Purendra Dehuri, Bisipada, 2012.

Offering to the earth goddess. Mati Puja

As a village of the Kandhamal, Bisipada must fulfil the demands of the earth goddess, even though it is not exclusively a Kond village. An annual ritual for the goddess is held in the hope of a good harvest. Earlier human sacrifices were carried out. Like many other villages in the region, Bisipada still has a 'meriah bush' where the sacrifices took place. A tree under which the hands of the last meriah victim are buried serves as the current ritual site. Today, the goddess is appeased by an animal sacrifice. The priest of the earth, a Kond or Kond potter, apologises to the goddess for the lack of a human offering.

Purendra Dehuri , priest
of the earth, behind
sits the adikari Jayadev
Bisoi. With the village
dignitaries around him,
the priest of the earth
conducts the offering
for the earth Goddess,
Bisipada, 2012.

Drumming festival,
Bisipada, circa 1953.

Drumming and dancing festival

The annual drumming festival is another event which
both Tina Otten and F.G. Bailey were able to witness.

Drumming festival,
Bisipada, 2013.

Domestic and life-cycle rituals
Drumming and dancing festival

169 F.G. Bailey's view
of the performance
was in Warrior Street,
Bisipada, 1950s.

Goma Purnima

Airborne: Malaya Ranjan
Bisoi catches a prize,
Bisipada 2012.

Domestic and life-cycle rituals
Goma Purnima

Futures

TOMORROW
CAN BE DREADFUL

Environmental awareness
campaign poster,
Gujarat, 2002.

Recovering in a
specialist hospital
after surgery,
Gujarat, 2002.

Tomorrow can be dreadful

In the 1950s, it was claimed that industrialisation and urbanisation was an 'exotic growth', super-imposed on an underdeveloped country, which had done nothing to ease the sometimes-painful conditions of rural life.

In time, the politics of the Cold War gave way to globalised agriculture. Technological innovation of seeds transformed yield and planting rhythms, as well as patterns of debt and corporate influence. Tractors have not, however, exterminated buffalo. Much of India continues to eat from the bent backs of women.

With electrification came light and groundwater; roads and vehicles brought mobility and carbon dependency. Televisions and mobile phones have altered what, how and when a villager can know about the world.

175

Hoarding for the popular
soft drink 'Thums Up',
Gujarat, 1999.

Grinding wheat, Jamgod, Madhya Pradesh, 2013.

The deregulation of land and infrastructure policy in India has allowed for a massive investment in a network of highways. Many of these are toll roads, which exclude rural populations on price and often quite literally run through the middle of rural populations.

Roads make it cheaper and easier to move people and goods, both in and out of rural areas: an algorithm without end. Madhya Pradesh, 2013.

The rural non-agricultural way of life

Agriculture is no longer the backbone of the village. Social hierarchies associated with farming have largely collapsed.

Affirmative action has often bettered the lot of the downtrodden.

Subsistence farming is rare. Global commodity markets unevenly shape what grows in the countryside. Agriculture is increasingly diverse: emus, chillies and energy.

People do other things, gamble, migrate, labour and speculate.

The countryside has been proletarianised and casualised. Farming has gone out of fashion.

The dreams of India's villagers have changed most of all, and often not in line with the material conditions or tangible possibilities of their existence.

Street scene, Jamgod,
Madhya Pradesh, 2013.

Top: Windfarm, Jamgod,
Madhya Pradesh, 2013.

Bottom: Based on
a 1924 German model,
the Hanseat Tempo has
been produced in India
by Bajaj from 1958.
The vehicle continues,
with modifications,
to keep much of rural
India moving, Jamgod,
Madhya Pradesh, 2013.

The rural non-agricultural way of life

The end of the village?

The idea that the city is superior to the countryside and that industrialisation is the antidote to inherent rural backwardness remains one of the most entrenched and resilient ideas on the planet. This is not only a conceit of metropolitan politics, it is a global master narrative.

The countryside is viewed from the window as the shrinking space between cities, traversed by urban-focused national infrastructures. City-dominated politics has turned rural India into a bloodstained battleground of planning and land deregulation, developer banditry, wind turbines, photovoltaic cells and mineral extraction. Today's paddy is tomorrow's gated community.

Some claim the village has gone. What remains? Exburbs, fringes, vicinities, brownfields, hermaphroditic and in-between sprawl? The city, in weak form, migrates to the village. A new pathway of human settlement and a relationship to land and space is being formed.

Sunrise over electricity infrastructure, Jamgod, Madhya Pradesh, 2013.

Top:
Collecting water
from the daily
tanker, Jamgod,
Madhya Pradesh, 2013.

Bottom:
Hoarding for digger
services, Jamgod,
Madhya Pradesh, 2013.

The end of the village?

Countryside = 'environment'?

Some environmentalists today take the view that
we must rethink what we mean by development
and progress. The global idea of development has
failed and reinforced older inequalities.

When we talk of 'environmental degradation' or
'the effects of global warming' where do we have
in mind? Generally, we are not referring to the city,
but the non-city of which the rural world forms the
greater part.

Gandhi's ideal of a village-based society with
fewer needs, different ambitions, and small-scale
subsistence production remain relevant as an
alternative. New experiments with village-living
are taking place in some parts of India today.

As with the Internet, there is an alternative
movement in India for organic, publically pollinated
and open access seeds, which, unlike F-1 hybrids
and GMO seeds, do not tie in farmers to annual
purchases from multi-nationals. These, however
optimistic, are mostly stories from the margins.

181

A painted picture of
the countryside passing
through the countryside,
Jharkhand, 2012.

In ways not so dissimilar to the 1950s, we may now ask what is the future of the rural world? The current configuration of rural life in India is increasingly resource intensive and exploitative. Some suggest that the city is the most sustainable form of settlement, which can be supported by exploiting the countryside more intensely.

In many countries, government spending per person tends to be lower in rural areas than urban ones. In this way, governments make the countryside poor. Hundreds of millions of people live below various measures of poverty line, at the bottom of the pyramid in what is becoming a vast rural suburb.

The Indian state is currently rolling-back traditionally protective policies towards land and the downtrodden, as the distinction between the city and the countryside begins to find its way in the country is governed. Are we with Gandhi, Nehru, Ambedkar or someone else?

182

"God knows", Jamgod, Madhya Pradesh, 2012.

The future: Slum to suburb?

Sealed Air ▷
Food Care
CRYOVAC®

in Expo Milano 2015
ffd coop
FUTURE FOOD DISTRICT

Print Your Meal ™

183

Italy: The Coop in the Future Food District of the Milan EXPO 2015 displayed anticipatory visions of technology which would allow consumers to 'Print a Meal' ™.

New Holland: a company which manufactures agricultural machinery, put up the only display to deal with the global picture of population growth and the changing balance of urban and rural populations. The marketing slogan for the New Holland Turbo Super 3500 in India is: The choice of every powerful farmer.

WORLD POPULATION

1927
2 Billion

1960
3 Billion

1987
5 Billion

1999
6 Billion

2015
7.2 Billion

Global food production must increase
72% by **2050** to meet our needs

Social dynamics of non-farm economy: A study of two 'rural' settlements of Madhubani District, Bihar

Surinder S. Jodhka

These photographs were taken during a field study of two large "rural" settlements, Satghara (formally a Census Town) and Bhagwatipur (a rural cluster with 10,000 plus population) in the Madhubani district of Bihar during the second half of 2014.

As is the case with most rural settlements in India, the households across both the settlements are divided into a wide range of caste groups and communities.

Caste-based communities mostly live in their own localities, known as tolas or paras. The tolas are also named after the titles of the community. While some localities do have mixed-caste populations, they are few. This was particularly so with the Dalit and Muslim localities.

We were able to identify a total of 1,680 individuals employed in different categories of non-farm activities, of which 1,384 were in Satghara and another 296 in Bhagwatipur. A large majority of

Social dynamics of non-farm economy: A study of two 'rural' settlements of Madhubani District, Bihar

the non-farm activities are typically individual centric
and self-owned enterprises. Those engaged in these
activities are relatively young men, below the age of 45
(76%) and many of them have had the experience of
working outside the state as migrant workers (48%).

Non-farm economy is largely a male enterprise,
with women making for a minuscule proportion of
the total employment in the category. The number
of women owning and managing an enterprise
on their own is not more 3 or 4 percent. Those
women engaged in non-farm economy tend to
work in occupations that are either traditionally
identified with women, such as bangle making,
or in occupations that involve serving exclusively
or primarily women, such as tailoring or running
a beauty parlor for women or vegetable vending.
Some of them also "help" their men but they tend to
be "invisible". Those engaged in non-farm economy
tend to be employed in low-income occupations and
come from relatively poorer families, lower OBCs or
Dalits, but none amongst the Muslims.

The social organization of different occupations largely remains structured around caste and community. Community and caste diversity exists only in certain categories of non-farm occupations. These include activities such as cell phone repair, modern electronic and communication related services, vehicle repair, medicine-related occupations, vegetable and fruit sellers and drivery/transport. Here too, we can easily observe community specific exclusions in some of the occupational categories. For example, there is no Scheduled Caste (SC) respondent in information technology, cell phones or communication related occupations. Similarly, we find very few Muslims, SCs or women in relatively modern categories or high investment oriented occupations, such as those related to medicine and health, education or construction and hardware. Even though a range of communities own grocery and other utility shops, they are dominated by relatively upper and trading castes that have been traditionally involved with such work.

Social dynamics of non-farm economy: A study of two
'rural' settlements of Madhubani District, Bihar

The same holds good for food related outlets, which tended to be owned by individuals from specific castes and communities.

Apart from visible and not-so visible divisions and differences of non-farm activities in accordance with the logic of traditional hierarchies of caste and communities, we also noticed active discrimination against some communities in relation to certain occupations (Muslims and Dalits).

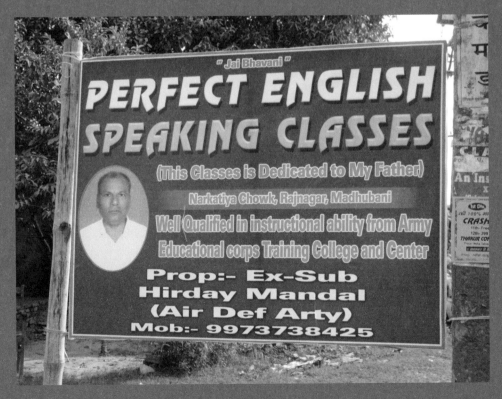

Social dynamics of non-farm economy: A study of two
'rural' settlements of Madhubani District, Bihar

The village is the Panna District of Madhya Pradesh, close to the UNESCO heritage site at Khajuraho. The village is surrounded by heavy forest, which is increasingly controlled by the state. The village is home to a 'tribal community', the Gonds. They are facing increasing restrictions on their use of forest resources. Displacement is a possibility in the future. The Gonds are both land-poor and income-poor. Due to the regulation of the forest, industry is not allowed in the area. As a result, circular and seasonal migration is necessary to supplement their incomes, many houses remain locked and empty for eight months of the year.

189

Social or cultural anthropology is an academic and humanistic discipline dedicated to the study and understanding of people, places and processes. Anthropologists generally explore what other people do, say, think, believe and how they act towards and with one another. For anthropologists, a series of meta-questions may follow such preliminaries: once these things have been identified what does it then *mean* to do, say, think, believe and act in particular contexts.

It used to be said that anthropology was about understanding the 'native's point of view', or what it meant to have different ideas about god, death, nature, kinship and other aspects of life. Then, anthropologists tended to conduct their research in faraway places, often regarded as 'exotic' or 'primitive'. Today, the discipline, at least as mostly understood by members of this project (and there are other ways), inhabits a largely, although not entirely, non-exotic world and aims to go two steps further.

The first step is to realise that the 'natives' (whoever they maybe) are people with history. The minutiae of their daily lives are also influenced, in part or whole, by the structural conditions of the world. They may or may not understand or even be aware of these influences. The lives of those in villages in India are directed and shaped, for example, by the actions of the local and national state, but also by remoter entities such interest rates and transnational agricultural businesses. The point of view of the 'native' remains vitally important, but cannot be the whole story.

It follows of course that not all of the 'natives' know the same things, and indeed, might hold quite different views on a range of issues, including fundamental ideas related to politics, religion and morality, or the truths of village life. Getting to know the corpus of what people know of themselves, and how they categorise and relate different domains of knowledge, is a key part of the modern

190

anthropological project. There has also been the gradual unfolding realisation that the idea of a 'native', as with so many other categories in popular usage, is largely derived from the colonial experience.

Anthropology has struggled to de-exoticise the subjects of research, given the temporal legacies of past events and processes and the momentum of knowledge structures of the discipline. In other words, the organisational paradigms of privilege, hierarchy and race of the colonial world have lingered. In the process of attempting to divest this past, the range of subjects and geographies of anthropology have expanded and diversified. Anthropologists may now study 'natives' such as stockbrokers and artists, as probably and productively as they study tribes or death rituals. It is also unlikely that the word 'native' will now be found in use as a general signifier.

Modern anthropology tends to assume that people are fundamentally equal in their potentials and abilities (*ceteris paribus*): none are more primitive or existentially advanced than others. The idea that culture or civilization follows an evolutionary path has largely been discounted, or at least has begun to appear irrelevant. As a part of the process of flattening and homogenising the variations of humanity, the guilt of colonialism has been worked into a theoretical lather by some anthropologists. The froth often obscures our vision of sustained structural inequalities, disparities in opportunity and privilege, and differentiated access to power mechanisms. However, in most specific cases, the burden of anthropological effort draws attention to marginalization and inequality, as worthy and largely unquestioned aims.

Anthropology, as we generally understand it as a professional practice in western Europe, has developed guides for ethical research and terms of appropriate engagement. Universities too have established procedures to ensure that research is conducted in an open, honest and respectful fashion. These procedures are well and good, but often they also seem to be rooted in a guilt which is out of time with the actual procedures of the world.

Our global era is characterised by change and
uncertainty. Unethical and unscrupulous action is
often at the defining heart of public life. Centres of
power and influence are shifting, as is the nature of
power itself. Outdated mechanisms of international
governance have consistently failed to deliver
peace and security. Climate change and intensified
conflict over resources run deep in the politics of
the planet. Our cities are swelling, as agrarian crises
combined with the politics of food security and land
fundamentally alter the rural world. Non-sovereign
investors control the distribution and revenue of
key resources and critical infrastructures. Economic
policies have led to the decline in absolute poverty
and the rise of inequality in some regions. Popular
protest, armed struggle and militarised governance
form the backdrop to everyday life in many places.
Innovation in technology and finance are at the
forefront of both international diplomacy and how
ordinary people live and think. Villages in India
are on the frontline of many of these processes,
and although it is simply wrong to think of them
as isolated or primitive, development indicators
suggest that extreme poverty persists.

As the post-colonial world rearranges itself,
new ways of life, being and through are emerging.
New terrains of politics and economic possibility
are animating human relationships. In many parts
of the world, novel and revisionist history and
notions of citizenship and belonging are being
realigned with the new politics: the rise of political
nationalism in India being an apt example. The
borders and boundaries of older cartographies
are fading as the world is remapped using zones
of cooperation, walls, fences and law. Traditional
sources of information, media and scholarship
face both uncertain and exciting futures.

The second step of our anthropology has been
to identify and reflect on the kinds of cultural and
individual baggage an anthropologist might carry with
them. This questioning is not solipsistic, but intended
as an act of understanding to improve and enliven
the categories through which the anthropologist
apprehends and sees salience in the world.
This broad technique may also partially be used to
explain why anthropologists are interested in some

What is anthropology?

particular issues and places, rather than others.

The ideas which emerged through this project have been developed though two kinds of mediated reflection. In chronological rather than methodological significance these have been as follows. The first dialogue was with the lives and work of Adrian Mayer, F.G. Bailey and David Pocock and India of the 1950s. The second was with the inhabitants of Jamgod, Bisipada and Sundarana today. We would like to think that much of the material presented here has emerged from the conversations and concerns of people in the villages. We will also like to think that they would recognise themselves as well as their trials and tribulations in the way their villages have been represented here.

The project has also taught us that anthropologists and the work they produce have lasting effects in the places they study. There has been no dramatic revelation or scandal in our cases: no illegitimate children nor instances of enslavement or psychological experimentation. However, we encountered concrete and enduring memories of the original anthropologists themselves. We have also seen that the books they produced have become important cultural resources within the villages. The language and terms of description, as well as the characterisation of hierarchy, heroes and villains has fed-back quite directly into village life. We therefore invested considerable time and effort in translating and publishing some of the original anthropology into local languages so that it would be more widely accessible, and will aim to do so with what we produce in the future, including this exhibition.

Anthropologists conduct research, which they call 'fieldwork' (note the staid metaphor out of kilter with an era of agrarian crisis). Generally, it is reckoned that it takes around a year for an anthropologist starting out in their career to get to know a place or particular issues thoroughly enough to write about them convincingly (depending on the competence and persistence of the anthropologist rather than any magic or natural formula or cultural osmosis).

The main research method is called 'participant observation'. The double bind of the idea is, as the term suggests, that the anthropologist 'participates' in the life of the place being studied while also 'observing' what is going on. This method gives primacy to vision over other senses; authenticity, legitimacy and the verifiability of research is given by 'being there' or 'witnessing', along with all the interesting problems of 'perspective' that this approach brings with it. Participant observation may also be supplemented by interviews and other research techniques, such as asking people to maintain diaries, to record myths and oral history and collecting biographies. It is largely the results of such methods which informed the choices we eventually made about how to represent rural India in this exhibition.

Whilst in the field anthropologists keep 'fieldnotes', ideally writing a daily account of their activity, progress and findings. The accumulated record usually tells the story of how anthropologists gain experience in a particular place. They generally contain descriptions of everyday life (often called 'ethnography'), letters and field reports written to supervisors, hunches, notes on language, as well as a diary of the activities of the fieldworker. Given that anthropological fieldwork generally lasts around a year, fieldnotes can become substantial documents.

When their fieldwork comes to an end, anthropologists begin the task of analysing and 'writing up' their material. In a more general language, this might mean reflecting on things they have seen, done and understood whilst in the field and determining what is meaningful and important. Anthropological writing tends to be quite slow when compared to other humanities disciplines. Turning life into words is a difficult kind of translation, and to do this well is generally time-consuming. In my view, the deeper the analysis goes then a truer and more loyal it becomes to the original observations.

Perhaps each generation struggles to understand and to put into robust words the chief characteristics of the prevailing zeitgeist. We have found it difficult to describe the kind of world we live in and therefore the kind of anthropologists and people we are.

What is anthropology?

Convincing and solid answers to the following questions have not been easy to come by. What do we know of the world with certainty? Where is our 'bottom line'? What are the organisational ideas that allow us to think we understand what is going on? In attempting to answer these questions uncertainty has reflected back upon us.

As anthropologists, we have rooted answers to these questions in our research in particular locations, primarily in the villages you have seen in this catalogue. This is a common anthropological knowledge strategy: to let the 'ethnography' speak. It might be objected that externalising the realities in which one trades is merely to sidestep the difficulty we have in answering our own questions about the world. However, the time and effort that good anthropological research takes, tends to give anthropologists an unusually firm conviction in the truth claims of their research.

The conditions in which anthropological research is usually incubated therefore contain a heady mix of elements: discomfort with the history and structure of the discipline, an acute self-awareness and reflexivity, and a conviction in the continued worth and validity of the truths of anthropological research. Needless to say, these elements do not always sit comfortably together, but we tend to carry on regardless.

The issues raised above notwithstanding, the realities of village life, at least as constructed through the long-term participant observation, become the basis from which questions can be raised, themes elaborated and arguments made. In an anthropological view, narration and presentation are forms of politics.
There is no value neutral fact or singular reality, each and everything is associated with other facts and things in particular and malleable ways and is thus part of a constellation of meaning on the move. The choice to start or end a description at a particular point is based on ideas of causality which often lie outside the story itself. Where do we start a description of a village? The rich and poor or men and women, for example, necessarily have very different views. Whose view shall we privilege and to what consequence?

Additionally, a great deal of written anthropology, which might initially appear as description to the neophyte, is in fact usually a form of argument or polemic. Such arguments are often made with other texts, but usually with theoretical claims, rather than with the ethnography of others which tends to remain sacrosanct. The endless argument is generally thought of as a way of improving and refining what is known: ruining the world in order to remake it anew, or, alternatively, the apprentice turning to do away with the master (the master having created his own rival, the university corridor is no longer of sufficient capacity to contain their combined wisdom). It might be better however, instead of adopting a teleological view of knowledge piling up in bigger and better heaps, to see argument with past and rival anthropology as a way of coming to terms with a new and endlessly emerging world. When all is said and done, and whatever some anthropologists may think of their intellectual transcendence, their own ideas about the world, however decentred, are not detached from the unnamed realities of the present.

Anthropological writing has theory and schools of thought, which are often also difficult to discern and comprehend for the uninitiated. Certain ideas, styles of analysis and structures of thought have become associated with particular departments or groups of scholars. Some of these dispositions might be entwined within research methods themselves, such as a focus on material over social, or social over cultural, or language over non-verbal reasoning such as symbols. Others might be less defined, relating to where particular anthropologists see the significant keys to true understanding to be located. A focus on gender or class or state-society relations presupposes distinct (however inchoate) ideas about the significance and the relative importance of those kinds of relationships when held up against others. Many anthropologists might argue that their approach is holistic, but in practice the holism is always run through with selections, priorities, hierarchies and differentiated forms of saliences and meaning.

In sum, the methods of anthropology offer a humane and important way into understanding the lives and knowledge structures of other people. As with any method, there are strengths and weakness, as well as benefits and shortcomings. Anthropology is also an exceedingly specialised and self-referential form of writing, theory and argument, which unfortunately often obscures rather than reveals the world. The particularity of the method also means that anthropology, as I have suggested, is quite difficult to read for those outside the discipline. In some ways, anthropology has become a rather exotic form of knowledge in a world that is arguably moving towards the post-exotic.

Finally, it is also worth making the straightforward point that the villages we have studied cannot adequately represent all social change in India, let alone change on a greater scale. However, an anthropologist would claim that having deep insight into the lives of people in a particular place is of greater conceptual and practical worth than having a partial view of life in many such and similar places. It is also the case that the ideas of an agrarian crisis, a changing role and aesthetic for the countryside, and the diversification of livelihoods and aspirations resonates far beyond the shrines at the entrance gates to the three villages. Significantly, uncertainty is also evident in the ethnography. The future role of the village and welfare of its inhabitants no longer rests upon the hope of the next harvest. Uncertainties relating to water, land and income dominate the immediate future of the rural world. There is also hope, but hope is tellingly conceived as better or more than now: prosperity, abundance and infinite growth, which will not happen.

197

Edward Simpson

The aircraft carrier *Ark Royal* was constructed between 1935 and 1938 by Cammell Laird and Company at Birkenhead near Liverpool. At the time, the vessel was the most sophisticated and expensive of the British fleet. At the launch, it took four swings of the bottle to spill champagne on the hull. The vessel saw very active service during the Second World War. In 1941, she was torpedoed and sunk in the Mediterranean. Commissions of enquiry found the overly-complicated design to be both the reason for her legendary success in battle and the ultimate cause of her final journey to the seabed.

As a boy, F.G. Bailey sat on the dockside watching the gradual assembly of *Ark Royal*. He bestowed her name upon us, seeing similarities between the design and possible fortunes of the project and those of the ship.

The story of how the research project came into being is also inseparable from the research we have produced. I end our story with recalling how it began and developed, as a way of explaining how the categories, divisions and claims made in our material found a way into existence. The exhibition was in some ways our first draft of 'writing up' and incorporates the processes referred to above. The key differences were that we used images instead of words and, more significantly, anthropologists generally work alone in the 'field'; in contrast, and contrary to most of our training, this project involved a great deal of collaboration as a community of professional strangers came together.

198

We wrote our anthropology with images. Primarily trained as academics to write, we have used images and collections of images to tell stories. There are places in which we stray from the path and wander off into the woods. Generally, however, our approach in much of the exhibition has been a rather direct representation of arguments. Of course, as in written anthropology there has been room for metaphor and analogy. Each of us had different ideas about the relationship between images and words, just as each of us brought different philosophical and technical eyes to the creation of these images. The juxtaposition of these different conceptual combinations coincides with the geographical and temporal divisions of the material. This has the effect of making the boundaries between anthropological eyes quite clear across the geography of the exhibition.

In 2009 Adrian Mayer approached the anthropology department at SOAS to ask if we might be interested in undertaking a 'restudy' of a village in India. Mayer had been conducting research in the village since the early part of the 1950s, some twenty years before I was born. He rightly emphasised the longitudinal nature of his field data, which, in no small measure, is reflection of his own longevity and vitality.

Mayer was born in 1922. He studied at the London School of Economics, conducting research in Malabar in the 1940s, before starting doctoral work in Fiji in 1950. Later, he held a research post in Australian National University. During his time there, he started the research he now wanted me to 'restudy'. In 1955, Jamgod had a population of 912 and was located in the state of Madhya Bharat, which is now Madhya Pradesh only a few kilometres from the industrial town of Dewas. Mayer conducted 15 months of ethnographic research there between 1954 and 1956. At the end of this period in the field, he moved to a teaching post at SOAS, where he remained until retiring as Pro-Director in 1987.

In a remarkably open and forthright move, Mayer said that if the project took off then he would also provide personal support, as well as access to his field notes, diaries and photographic collection. All in all, this was a rather daunting proposition: Mayer had been a stalwart of the discipline and its professional institutions, a long serving and loyal member of SOAS, a rigorous fieldworker and an efficient and effective writer.

At about the same time, I also learned more about Mayer's meticulous fieldwork and record-keeping practices. He had counted and measured the village, conducting surveys and examining land records.

He had taken copious notes and written summative reports. He also kept a diary. In this, of course, he is not alone because these are the standard techniques used by many anthropologists. However, I think it fair to say that Mayer has an unusual capacity to remember and describe the world. He also, and clearly from an early age, had developed a similarly extraordinary approach to documentation and record-keeping. His archive is exact and tidy and, therefore, relatively accessible.

After some deliberation, I decided to take up Mayer's invitation. However, in order to secure adequate funds for the project I also thought it best to enlarge the scope and to conduct other restudies in parallel. This would, I then reasoned, provide a comparative account and would allow us to examine different kinds of development trajectory and contrasting stories of social change, it would also allow us to think anew about methodology and the history of the British sociology of India.

I had then been thinking about the modern history of the anthropology of India and had contributed to a review of the work of David F. Pocock following his death in 2007. I wondered if the village in which Pocock had conducted research in the 1950s might also fit the bill. To restudy the village in which he had worked in Gujarat presented rather a different proposition to that suggested by Mayer. Pocock obviously could not help us himself; furthermore, he had left very few personal traces, having deliberately burned his fieldnotes notes on a bonfire in his garden when he retired from the University of Sussex.

Jonathan Parry and Edward Simpson, 2010. 'David Pocock's contributions and the legacy of Leavis.' *Contributions to Indian Sociology*, 43(3): 331–359

In 2010, I went to Sundarana to see for myself whether it would be a productive place to restudy. I had no idea what to expect of either the village or the marks left by Pocock. Part of me perhaps hoped there would be a statue of him in the village square or a library or dovecote put up in his name. There was nothing. During the brief day I spent there I met nobody who remembered him, nor anyone who thought academic research was worthwhile. But later I learned, and as a strict testament to the power of ethnographic fieldwork over less rigorous and less time-consuming methods, that memories of Pocock still inhabited the village. Pocock was, it turned out, well remembered.

From my own first fleeting visit, I left with the impression that the village was full of life, and run through with significant disparities of wealth and privilege. The quality of housing varied considerably. All around verdant and fertile fields seemed to tell a story of prosperity. Nearby, were some of the wealthiest villages in India, from where migrants had settled overseas and now formed extensive transnational networks through which goods, politics and religion flowed in abundance. I also felt that rural Gujarat had been neglected somewhat in very recent times, with more books, and certainly more attention on the state's violent and casualised cities.

David F. Pocock (1928 – 2007) read English at Cambridge, where he was influenced by the then well-known literary criticism and social philosophy of F.R. Leavis. At Oxford, Pocock wrote on the Nilotic tribes of Sudan. For his doctoral work, he focused on the 'Asians' (Gujaratis) in East Africa. The experience later took him as a post-doctoral researcher to Gujarat in search of more 'authentic' Indians. Between 1953 and 1956 he spent around eighteen months in the village of Sundarana (then part of Bombay State), also conducting complementary research in the nearby villages of Dharmaj and Gorel.

David Pocock, 1972. *Kanbi and Patidar: A study of the Patidar community of Gujarat.* Oxford: Clarendon. 1973. *Mind, body and wealth: A study of belief and practice in an Indian village.* Oxford: Basil Blackwell.

Pocock was appointed to a lectureship at Oxford in 1955, moving to the University of Sussex in 1966, where he remained until retirement. While at Balliol or Oxford-on-Sea, as Sussex was then known, Pocock published two monographs on his 1950s fieldwork in Sundarana, one of these was about marriage and status, the second was about popular Hinduism.

Finding a third anthropologist to restudy, around whom a plausible individual and comparative case could be made, took slightly longer. In the end, one of my own doctoral supervisors, Johnny Parry, suggested I write to F.G. Bailey, who he had last heard of at the University of California, San Diego.

I did, of course, as Parry suggested. I asked Bailey outright if and how he would support a restudy of Bisipara in Highland Orissa where he had conducted research throughout the 1950s. Clearly not perturbed by the cold calling, and to my delight, Bailey was instantly enthusiastic about the idea. He wrote back immediately offering:

...a cupboard full of handwritten surveys of fields, their yields, ownership, hours worked in them, hand-drawn maps, house censuses, various texts (all in Oriya, a few translated), a book of genealogies, household surveys, etc etc, all on crumbling bazaar-bought foolscap paper. Some photographs, 35mm negatives, last looked at when I gathered photos to put in *The witch hunt* [1994]... you can have complete access to everything...

Bailey also invited me to visit him in California, an invitation I took him up on a year later and again in the following year. He spoke openly for many hours, and often on camera, about his fieldwork and career in anthropology. His initial description of the material was understated. He gave us access to thousands of pages of field notes, surveys and work and farming diaries. Perhaps most interesting to read but hardest to use productively were his own notes of key learnings, suspicions, hunches and emerging lines of enquiry.

Together, both Bailey and Mayer gave us access to far more material than we could practically be expected to use thoughtfully within the timeframe of the project.

Bailey was born in 1924. He read classics at Oxford, and saw active service towards the end of the

Second World War; both experiences left marks. He joined University of Manchester for his doctoral research and started his teaching career at SOAS in 1956. Later he moved to the University of Sussex and, later still, to the University of California San Diego, where he remained until retirement.

F.G. Bailey, F.G. 1957. *Caste and the economic frontier: A village in highland Orissa;* 1960. *Tribe, caste, and nation: A study of political activity and political change in highland Orissa.* Both: Manchester: Manchester University Press; 1963. *Politics and social change; Orissa in 1959.* Berkeley: University of California Press.

F.G. Bailey, 1994. *A witch-hunt: In an Indian village or, the triumph of morality;* 1996. *The civility of indifference;* 1998. *The need for enemies: A bestiary of political forms.* All three: Ithaca: Cornell University Press.

203

Bailey conducted his principal fieldwork in the villages of Bisipara (then population 700) and smaller 'Baderi' (properly Boida) in the highlands of Orissa between 1952 and 1955 and again in 1959. He wrote three ethnographic monographs based on his village research during his time at SOAS (1957, 1960, 1963). These describe and analyse social change at the level of the village, caste and regional politics. He intended these to be heavyweight interventions (and they were) in the key debates of the day. In the 1990s, he revisited his own Bisipara research with three further retrospective books (1994, 1996 and 1998), written from a comfortable chair in California.

Patricia Jeffery became the Co-Investigator on the project. We wrote an application to the Economic and Social Research Council (ESRC), the social science funding body of the United Kingdom. The application was successful and we were then faced with the difficult task of recruiting three post-doctoral researchers. We were confounded by the number of young scholars with doctorates and relevant research experience who responded to our advertisement.

We had probably unconsciously assumed that we would work with South Asian scholars, for political and practical reasons. In the end, and due to forces beyond our control, we recruited two Italians and a German, two were women and one was a man. Each had been schooled in a different anthropological tradition and fieldwork techniques. Importantly, each came with experience of local languages and fieldwork in the relevant parts of India, and burgeoning enthusiasm for the project. In time, each of the post-doctoral researchers developed their own relationships with their predecessors,

the research and the villagers. These are not my
stories to tell, although I cannot resist brief comment.

Adrian and Tommaso were fortunate to be able
to spend a considerable amount of time together
discussing the project generally and field notes
and research in particular. Adrian had some rather
clear ideas about what the restudy should entail.
The new fieldwork should be based on an extensive
household survey and investigate the questions
and trends that Adrian had identified in the village
over the decades. Tommaso was moved by both
Marxist and post-structuralist ideas of the world.
For him, the realities of village life were perhaps
less certain than they had been for Adrian. However,
this shoulders were broad enough to take on quite
directly the demands that Adrian placed upon him.
I think that Tommaso also learnt to see that Adrian's
rendering of the village was based on a deep
awareness that people had different perspectives,
but that a holistic triangulation of these differences
could in some ways represent a cogent whole in
which not all had the same power or influence.
In the end, the two grew close, both admitting
touching bonds of indebtedness and affection.

The hands of Adrian
Mayer (left) and Tommaso
Sbriccoli at work in the
fieldnotes, London, 2012.

204

David Pocock passed away in 2007. Alice had only his legacy to build a relationship with. She had never met him, nor paid much attention to his anthropology. She was able to read his books and papers, and in the process imagine him as an individual and as part of a broader community of scholars. Looking at this relationship from the outside, I could see a strong affinity between the ways they both liked to think. Ambiguity, partiality and an acknowledgement that things were always in the making and negotiable rather than rule-bound and set in stone animated their anthropology. In the field, Alice was confronted perhaps more directly than she anticipated by Pocock's ghost. In time, people came forward who had quite clear memories of him. He was provided with a routine, a place to live, friends and personal characteristics. The fields and lanes of Pocock's ethnography gradually began to reveal themselves, as she learned to see the village as he had done.

Tina and Freddy were separated by the Atlantic. Tina was fortunately able to spend two weeks with him at his home in California to discuss his life and work. We also had access to his field notes and photographic collection which proved to be a tremendous resource. I was not to know before the project got underway, but Freddy had academic contact with Tina's own supervisor and mentor in Berlin, Georg Pfeffer. Their exchange had been acrimonious, and Freddy's contribution remained unpublished. Tina clearly felt uncomfortable and experienced different tugs of loyalty in the middle of such silverback rivalry. I am, however, getting ahead of myself, and I will return to the significance this rivalry later. Tina's own interests were also in some ways antithetical to those Freddy. He was interested in land and politics, believing them to be the single-most influential domains in determining how things really were. In contrast, Tina was drawn to religion, ritual and myth, topics Freddy possibly considered frivolous (and indeed are not well represented in his notes), but in which Tina saw unique and powerful meaning. However, Tina was able to loyally follow some of the hypotheses and topics that Freddy himself had written about, and adding to this her own interests she was able to broaden the scope of both investigation and analysis.

Once the project got underway, we convened
regularly at SOAS, often with Adrian Mayer. We held
a series of seminars and workshops on rural India
and the methods best suited to restudying things.
We held a memorable session at the Lisbon meeting
of the European Conference of South Asian Studies
in 2012, to which we were able to invite a whole
host of scholars well known for their long-term
engagements with questions of rural change.
We also presented our initial ideas at the Centre
for Social Studies in Surat (CSSS) and at various
venues in Delhi, Mumbai and elsewhere in Gujarat.

Over the following three years, the strengths
and weaknesses of a comparative restudies
project became increasingly pronounced.
Our initial discussions had helped focus our
attention, fieldwork helped to further refine
the focus, and as we came to write up the
project we encountered new kinds of issues.
One of the greatest challenges we faced was
understanding not *what* but *how* and *why* the
three anthropologists wrote what they did.
On one level, we had to think about the discipline
of anthropology at the time and what kinds of
theory were fashionable. All three had an interest
in land, seeing power to lie in its holding. Bailey was
interested in the analysis of dispute, Mayer in the
holistic understanding of the village and Pocock
(although he wrote up his material much later)
pursued the ideas of contingency and partiality of
explanation. All three were influenced by theories
of lineages and affinity which were fashionable at
the time, a point to which I return later. Mayer and
Bailey were fascinated by what would happen to
villages in the new political set-up of Independent
India; in contrast, Pocock barely acknowledges
a world outside the village.

Theoretical debate in anthropology has shown how
long-term studies necessarily shift the emphasis
of analysis from stasis to change, undermining the
sureties of the 'ethnographic present' and 'being
there'. Time changes things and not always in a
logical or predictable fashion; things do not always
have trajectories, in any straightforward sense.
Numerous anthropologists and economists have
traced shifts in rural life through their own long-

term research engagements. In this, Susan Wadley's longitudinal research in Uttar Pradesh stands out for provocatively outlining the emergence of a general spirit of optimism in the post-colonial decades, alongside the loss of power among the traditional elite, and growing disparities of wealth.

Susan Wadley, 2001
Behind mud walls:
Seventy five years in
a North Indian village.
Berkeley: University
of California Press.

Two features distinguish *Ark Royal* from previous studies. The first is the comparative aspect (three states and three different original baseline studies); the second is the rather straightforward fact that two of the three original researchers were alive and enthusiastic. The project was, therefore, intended to be a novel experiment in practical comparative field methodology and inter-generational ethnography, which built on the insights of long-term field engagements of others and the accumulated results of repetitious visits to the same fields. We also conceived of this project as a contribution to a discipline, a means of consolidating past effort – where data of known provenance could be used to measure change.

207

Significantly, then, what distinguished this project from others is the fact that Bailey and Mayer were not only alive and well, but also volunteered their time and materials to actively participate in the project. It is one thing to restudy the work of somebody who is dead, and who cannot argue back, and whose feelings cannot be hurt; it is quite another to work alongside living anthropologists, whose reputation and opinions play quite directly into the research itself. Likewise, it is one thing to read someone's fieldnotes in an archive or library, but it is quite another to have the author of those fieldnotes explain and elaborate. I do not think it coincidental that some of the first publications to emerge from the research have been on Gujarat, where we have not had access to fieldnotes or the spoken word of David Pocock.

Anthropologists are not generally trained to work in teams. Quite the opposite, they are usually taught solitary fieldwork techniques, in which field relationships are about generating research data, rather than professional cooperation.

Therefore, working so intimately with one another proved something of an epistemological as well as interpersonal challenge.

We also had to be mindful of the fact that the views of the original anthropologists on both the project and the value and worth of anthropology more generally were cast in a very different time. Specifically, anthropology is a much more self-aware discipline today than it was some six decades hence. Over the last few years, we have seen that not all members of the team share a unified vision of the aims and objectives, let alone methods, of anthropology as an academic practice.

There were also questions of a more practical nature. How were we to treat confidential or controversial information contained in their field notes in the field? How would we even know if the things anthropologists recorded as significant in the 1950s continued to form or influence part of village life today? How were we to treat the original material in relation to contemporary research practice which necessitates confidentiality and anonymity? What were we to do if there were Malinowski-diary moments? Malinowski (1967) was one of the founders of modern anthropology. He had famously kept a diary separate to his field notes, in which he recorded his personal thoughts and desires. When published, posthumously, the material cast what some have seen as a sceptical shadow over his claims to a scientific method.

Bronislaw Malinowski, 1967. *A diary in the strict sense of the term*. New York: Harcourt, Brace&World.

As a team, we had six field-working anthropologists to compare, Bailey, Mayer, Pocock and the three post-doctoral researchers who conducted the 'restudy' work, Tina Otten, Tommaso Sbriccoli and Alice Tilche. These relations and the slippages between them were mediated by myself as Principal Investigator and Patricia Jeffery as the Co-Investigator, an anthropologist and anthropologist-cum-sociologist respectively; therefore, methodological and reflexive debate and awareness became central component of the initial months of the project.

Rather than treating the original ethnographies as either beyond empirical scrutiny or as a

subjective fiction, we worked to understand
the processes that brought them into being.
We attempted to identify the methodological
techniques and theoretical devices of the original
anthropologists and reflected similarly on the
practices of the 'restudying' anthropologists in a
more general sense. In fact, however, the activities
and techniques of their fieldwork became much
clearer once the team itself started work in the field.

From the 1980s, the critical work on the politics
of representation and the role of subjectivity
in anthropological research has grown apace.
This literature has critically considered how age,
gender, ethnicity and class influence the ways
people interact with the anthropologist in the
field and how 'informants' are willing to share their
lives. The point to emerge from these important
debates as we understood them within the project
was that it was not going to be possible to conduct
a 'carbon copy' of the original fieldwork; nor, we
concluded, was solely aiming to do so the most
interesting or intellectually productive objective.
No one in the modern discipline of social/cultural
anthropology/Indian sociology believes that the
generation of anthropological data can be simply
separated from the personal traits and relative
competence or diligence of the anthropologist.
This is not to say, however, that there is no
point in trying to ask the same questions as the
original anthropologists did. Such questions were
obviously going to yield their own significant and
comparable data, but they would also allow the
researchers to begin to see the villages broadly as
their predecessors might have done. We reasoned
that we could then test their general propositions
and hypotheses and re-assess the validity of the
original claims in the light of the new data.

At another level, the introspective gaze on the
epistemological practices of the discipline made
us mindful of the frames and assumptions included
in the presentation of the lives of others. We also
discovered published criticisms and reviews of the
work of Bailey, Mayer and Pocock, both specific
and general, and of some of the limitations inherent
to the kind of questions they asked. For example,
their general focus on agnatic kin in villages only

represents the social relations of the villagers in one particular way to the exclusion of others.

Also influential on our plans were debates on the cultural history of the prominent role of caste in anthropological writing on India and the disentanglement of this intellectual concern from empirical realities on the ground. To put this simply, was their focus on caste a straightforward reflection of the significance of the institution to village life? Or, was it also part of the intellectual fashions of the moment? Of course, it was probably both of these things, but it is far from easy to untangle such divergent rationales when looking back in time. Similarly, but in a different register, there is no mention of the Partition of India in any of the published work. Does this mean that Partition was not important in the villages of India at the time, less than five years after those tragic events? Or, does it mean that the anthropologists of the period focused on, and saw legitimacy and authenticity in, village matters? Big politics were perhaps better left to the political scientists.

Such issues are perennial in anthropology and cannot be put to sleep by simple answers. Issues such as these also came to the fore in the spat between the silverbacks of the anthropology of Odisha, between Georg Pfeffer and F.G. Bailey. In the 1950s, anthropologists spent a great deal of time and ink in debating the role 'descent' and 'alliance' (sometimes called 'diachronic affinity') played in patterning relationships between descent groups. In time, that debate was abandoned, unsettled, like so many anthropological arguments, because it quickly reached the outer limits of the mind. In the literature, this impassioned debate was presented as being about the ways in which certain people in Africa and Asia constructed an understanding of themselves and their relationships with others. In contrast, and as F.G. Bailey pithily put it, this debate was concerned with nothing that was ontologically real other than the methodological preferences of the scholars involved.

F.G. Bailey, unpublished: 'The totality-itch: A commentary on Dr. Pfeffer's view of Kond society', p. 15. A commentary on Georg Pfeffer, 1997. 'The Scheduled Tribes of Middle India as a unit.' In Georg Pfeffer and Deapak Kumar Behera (eds) *Contemporary Society, Tribal Studies. Volume 1, Structure and Process*. New Delhi: Concept, pp. 3-27.

Arguably, this remains the condition of much of the more-opinionated anthropology of our times.

Georg Pfeffer is a German anthropologist who has studied parts of Odisha for most of his life. He ran a series of large projects involving many researchers, and as he did so the tone and focus of his interest necessarily moved from the specific to the general and comparative. In a volume published in 1997, Pfeffer attempted to correct the errors, as he saw them, that had crept into the ethnographic record on Odisha, including Bailey's account of descent and lineage in the highlands.

Perhaps taken by the mood in America at that moment, F.G. Bailey sat down on September 12, 2001 to respond to Pfeffer's piece. He characterised the world as populated by foxes and hedgehogs. Foxes knew many things; hedgehogs know one big thing and suffer from 'the totality-itch'. Rage or perhaps indignation was evident in this tone. Pfeffer suggested that Bailey had seen lineages amongst the tribal people of the highlands where there were none to be seen. In Bailey's words:

211

> Dr Pfeffer asserts that after re-examining "Bailey's Kondh data" he can "discard the structural-functionalist lineage theory and apply the structuralist alliance theory". My response will be that he misunderstands and therefore misrepresents my use of structural functionalist theory; and that when he applies the structuralist alliance theory he creates an imaginary sociocultural entity that departs markedly from the social structure of the Balimendi Konds.

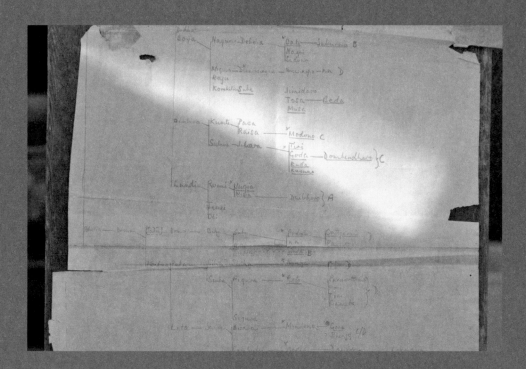

In sum, Pfeffer suggested that the Konds are uninterested in genealogy and that Bailey found genealogy because that is what he asked them about. In reply, Bailey suggested Pfeffer has hedgehog-like tendencies in his thinking, a trait which causes the mind to lose as much in accuracy as it gains in comprehensiveness.

The dispute between descent and alliance theorists has arisen periodically and repeatedly in the history of anthropology. Unpicking such a tight knot quickly leads into an unnavigable philosophical terrain in which the nature of knowledge itself is on the line. How do we know others for certain? In some ways, this question concerns all of us all the time, but for the anthropologist it is also a matter of professional identity, methodology and integrity. Longevity does not bring a more certain answer to the problem.

More than once during this project, Mayer expressed his doubts about the wisdom of having embarked on such a course. He told me that it was such a long time ago, that he could no longer remember how he knew things about the village with so much certainty. 'What' he said 'if I just made it all up?' Bailey too, after his initial and unbridled

Sunset dapples the highland genealogies in F.G. Bailey's fieldnotes, San Diego, 2012.

212

enthusiasm for the project, began to have some doubts. 'What are you going to do' he asked 'if you discover I am a charlatan?'

I have often wondered why anyone should have been surprised by Malinowski's diary. It shows him to be a distinctly human kind of human being, and anyone who thought of him as otherwise can only have themselves to blame. I think however the sense of doubt both Bailey and Mayer expressed in their own lives and works can be taken as a lead into a more profound point about truth, method and time. They were both copious note takers and enthusiastic fieldworkers and the idea that they made anything up simply does not accord with the demonstrable relationship between the initial tentative field notes, the more refined condensations of these in reports and summaries, and the books they finally wrote.

However, over the course project it became quite clear to me that what they thought they remembered most about their fieldwork was actually not the act of fieldwork, but what they had chosen, wilfully or not, to write about it. Even then, what they remembered most vividly were the arguments they put forth in the most condensed form in their published work.

I found this to be one of the most interesting if casual realisations of the methodological backstory to the whole project. That by writing, first field notes and later books and papers, you are giving personal memory an architecture. You are dividing the world in particular ways, and, in time, those ways become confused with memories and they become memory itself. This was particularly true for Bailey, who for various reasons, some desperately unfortunate, had not returned to his field site since the 1950s. This was less so for Mayer because he had returned to the village on a number of occasions, at least once a decade, and most recently as part of this project. It was almost as if the sense they had made from the field became the reality of the village in their descriptions. Of course, the village had influenced the sense they had made from it, but the partial renderings and occasional and sporadic snapshots of village life they both relied upon, could

213

not easily be presupposed to represent all of a
greater reality.

—

Today, some scholars have suggested that the
Indian village is a redundant economic unit. In this
view, the agrarian economy has withered in the face
of rising rates of rural-urban migration: the village
has become a vicinity. While this characterisation
might perhaps be overstating the case, the argument
draws dramatic attention to how rural India has
changed since the 1950s.

The villages in our project display the signs,
institutions and buildings of post-colonial
development and political policies, the
consequences of economic and land reform,
and the burdens of an expanding population.
As is well-known, land has fragmented,
contributing to the impossibility of making
a sustainable living from agriculture.

These are also sites in which novel and significant
sociological processes are being played out today.

In each location, there has been a growth and
consolidation of grassroots Hindu nationalist
politics. In Odisha, land rights and tribal identities
have become burning issues, as people have
been brought into conflict with transnational
corporations and rapacious extractive industries.
Rapid industrialisation in Madhya Pradesh has
brought villagers into wage relations with India's
industrial houses and the boom town of Dewas.
In Jamgod, a once-lowly Muslim community has
grown, and grown wealthy, and now dominates
many facets of village life. In Gujarat, the village
has become part of the transnational networks
and nostalgic and nationalist politics of Patidar
migrants in East Africa and UK, and the Muslims
were banished in 2002 and their mosque vandalised.
Life in these villages is clearly subject to different
kinds of broad influence and pressure from when they
were studied in the 1950s. Political parties, unions
and nationalist and civil movements play significant
roles. The three case studies also very clearly remind
us of the impossibility and dangers of generalising
about the rural world, as if it were a homogeneous

and identifiable set of conditions or qualities. Thinking across the case studies has allowed us to clearly see the value of disaggregating the idea of 'the countryside' and likewise a 'rural sociology'.

Anthropological writing about the Indian village of the 1950s did much to move theories of social change away from mechanistic, teleological and evolutionary development schemes, towards an emphasis on human agency, an acceptance of the contingency of events, and the study of multiple and relative modernities. At the time, anthropologists took the Indian village as a self-contained fieldsite (although not often as a self-evident unit of analysis) and attempted to measure and understand aspects of life there, often conducting thorough and extensive surveys of households and land-holding. The records they produced in their ethnographic writing now form an intimate kind of historic source material; a status which, although valuable and novel, must be accompanied by qualification and methodological reflection.

In the 1950s, anthropologists clearly saw that farming could no longer form the backbone of the village economy. According to them, there would be an increase in other forms of employment, and a corresponding shift in traditional patterns of hierarchy and inequality. The influence of land, at least on the scale of the village, was inevitably to lose ground to commercial acumen and cash wealth. They also saw that the enlarging state and the influence of legislation on village ways would change the horizons and traditional patterns of hierarchy, which so characterised life in rural India. Affirmative action policies and land reforms in particular were unsurprisingly anticipated as having dramatic consequences of village life.

Anthropologists at the time could see that rural India was in the midst of radical change. Specifically, Mayer saw that increasing pressures on land in the village of Jamgod would lead to fundamental shifts in the agrarian economy and augment dependency on nearby towns for livelihoods. Pocock predicted that the hierarchy of caste in Central Gujarat would wane, as the principles of purity and pollution ordering inter-caste relationships crumbled, along with the

traditional relationships of the agrarian way of life
and the increasing popularity of congregational
Hinduism. In Bisipada, Bailey foresaw that alternative
occupations would emerge as large families resulted
in the fragmentation of landholdings. Traders would
rise in wealth and power over the old landowners.

John Bailey, F.G.
Bailey's son, became
a farmer, South of
France, 2012.

216

I find it noteworthy that the predictions made in
the 1950s have remained the key and sometimes
repetitive findings of the subsequent six decades
of rural studies, in India but also elsewhere. In sum,
the countryside has been hollowed out, farming
has ceased to provide an income for most, and
dirty finger nails have gone out of fashion;
livelihoods have diversified; migration and other
forms of petro-mobility have increased.

There appears to have been something in the air.
The Anthropological Survey of India (a government
department) also started an industrial scale 'restudies'
project at about the same time. This effort included
the villages in which both Bailey and Mayer worked.
Thus it was that during our research, we met teams of
anthropologists from the Survey in both Jamgod and
Bisipada. They were working within an inter-disciplinary
framework but were asking many of the same

questions as us. They too were drawn to the villages on the basis of previous anthropological investigation.

The Indian anthropologists we met in Bisipada were a team of biological, psychological and social anthropologists. The meeting was not an orchestrated way of taking anthropology back to the village, although that might have been provocative. Instead, it was a chance and unusual encounter which took place in the house of one of F.G. Bailey's former research assistants. In her excitement, the film maker/ research assistant who was travelling with us suddenly confused 'on' with 'off', so when she thought she was filming she was in fact not, and conversely when she put the camera down to rest on her thigh she turned the camera on. The result is a partial soundtrack of the encounter and a few shots of the assembled when the camera was being moved up and down into filming or resting positions. By the way she moved through the crowd, she clearly thought she was doing a wonderful job of recording a rare moment, rich in interpretive possibility.

217

It was a hot day, with a powerful sun at full height in a clear blue sky. Chickens scratched in the dirt of the compound of the house where the encounter took place. It was suddenly obvious that no one quite knew what the protocol was in such circumstances. What were these 'groups' of anthropologists? Rivals? Professional friends? As anthropologists, we could probably all instantly see that we were at the confluence of different notions and continents of history, power and authority. But whose? And to what ends? Of more immediate concern was the matter of who was going to introduce who, given that we were all in someone else's house.

The bizarre outcome: members of each party spontaneously presented a brief summary of their qualifications and academic achievements along with their handshake and name: speed-dating with abbreviated professional curricula vitae. Meanwhile, a small crowd had gathered to watch the hastily ritualised encounter – some took pictures (using their technology correctly). Extracts from the soundtrack include: "if you are interested, I can submit your details or intentions to higher officials" and "Is your book available?" And, after it is all over: "The anthropologist 'filming' the anthropologists being filmed by the 'informants'" and "It was awesome. I loved it. Meta-anthropological."

To me, what appears like coincidence is more than that and suggests a new role and place for old ethnography within new research. Anthropology has become a measure of things, and can sensibly and productively be used as a historical resource. Like all archives, the material must be used with caution and an understanding of its strengths, weaknesses and original purposes; however, we have found that anthropology contains much certainty, if not to say 'reality', in any simple sense. The main problem with the archive is knowing what is certain and central, rather than serendipitous or peripheral or a limited product of that particular intellectual and political moment.

It is worth reflecting for a moment on why at least two separate governments should simultaneously decide that restudying anthropological work from the 1950s should be a worthwhile and fundable exercise. The 1950s is almost a lifetime ago, almost. The number of people who were alive during the great transition from colonial to post-colonial world is dwindling. First-hand access to those who lived through this momentous upheaval is disappearing. Perhaps, also, there is nostalgia for a time when the world was optimistic and enthusiastic about the future. It is also the case that rural India, as other parts rural world, is on the cusp of new and intense forms of social change. Looking backwards to the past, identifying trends and trajectories may also help us understand possible futures for the rural world.

In the end, we decided that it was better not to frame the projects only as 'restudies'. For one, we had little primary data for the intervening decades, more in the case of Jamgod – but very little for the other two sites. We have found the idea of 'doing the same fieldwork twice' to be more productive as an idea. The new researchers could not step in the footprints of a previous generation because the winds of change had blown many of those away. The villages had clearly changed too, and so therefore must the nature of our research questions. Juxtaposing the ethnography from the 1950s with that of today is not a subtle or respectful approach to the key transformations of the important post-colonial decades; neither does it allow us to say much about actual trajectories of change and continuity. However, the results are striking.

The trends identified in the 1950s as influencing the future direction of village life continue to define in a broad sense what village life is about and what it means to be a villager. With brevity, and glossing complexity and variation across the sites, the juxtaposition reveals in clear form that the role of agriculture and the material zand symbolic capital of small-scale land-holding has declined. Farming is now peripheral to many routines, rituals and prosaic concerns in these villages, most so in Gujarat and least so in Odisha. Livelihoods and agricultural production continue to diversify, and to a great extent farming has simply gone out of fashion. Caste hegemony remains, modified of course by various legislative measures, but other forms of ethnic and religious politics tend to dominate daily life. Religion in particular plays an important role in identity politics and has produced vertical schisms within rural communities. Significantly, this trend appears to have been entirely absent from the ethnography of the 1950s (not perhaps in Punjab or Bengal).

If we are to trust the ethnography, then other features of village life absent from the 1950s include: mass unemployment, 'over' education, and endemic cultures of 'waiting', suggesting that the culture, aspirations and frames of reference for villagers have changed quite fundamentally. Land fragmentation has combined with speculative land and construction markets to create new conflicts between agriculture and non-agricultural ways of rural life. Private monopolists or 'mafias' dominate many of the local supply chains, which we might imagine to have been property of the state in some of the intervening decades. Transnational capital has become increasingly sophisticated at extracting revenue from village markets. Service professions, a middle class and strangers have

219

properly entered rural life. Fundamentally, a mobility paradigm organises daily and longer term life-cycle expectations for many, including commuting and regional and international migration.

We also found that the village, however hollowed out in economic or residential terms, is regularly evoked as a unit of political mobilisation. Perhaps, however, this is primarily a product of the structures of democracy, rather than a primordial or meaningful expression of collective identity. Local government policy often seems out of step with the order of things. National government policy for rural areas seems increasingly to reflect private and corporate realities rather than defining them. Finally, in some key respects, the conceptual distinction between villages and cities appears to be fading, but agriculture has not gone away. Vocabularies of social science and public policy require reworking beyond labels such as 'post-agrarian' or 'rurban'. Such terms flatten the dense contours of the new landscape in which paddy grows amid the concrete and steel of novel industriousness.

Looking backwards in time at villages in India encouraged us to identify trends and trajectories, and eventually to ask questions about what the future might hold.

The veranda of the
house F.G. Bailey
occupied in Bisipada
in the 1950s, 2013.

On the making of Ark Royal

SOAS, University of London is the only Higher Education institution in Europe specialising in the study of Asia, Africa and the Near and Middle East.

SOAS is a remarkable institution. Uniquely combining language scholarship, disciplinary expertise and regional focus, it has the largest concentration in Europe of academic staff concerned with Africa, Asia and the Middle East.

On the one hand, this means that SOAS scholars grapple with pressing issues – democracy, development, human rights, identity, legal systems, poverty, religion, social change – confronting two-thirds of humankind while at the same time remaining guardians of specialised knowledge in languages and periods and regions not available anywhere else in the UK.

223

This makes SOAS synonymous with intellectual enquiry and achievement. It is a global academic base and a crucial resource for London. We live in a world of shrinking borders and of economic and technological simultaneity. Yet it is also a world in which difference and regionalism present themselves acutely. It is a world that SOAS is distinctively positioned to analyse, understand and explain.

Our academic focus on the languages, cultures and societies of Africa, Asia and the Middle East makes us an indispensable interpreter in a complex world.

Edward Simpson

Edward Simpson is Professor of Social Anthropology
at SOAS. His research interests include mobility,
catastrophe and infrastructure. He is the author of
The political biography of an earthquake: Aftermath
and amnesia in Gujarat, India (2013, Hurst).

Alice Tilche

Alice Tilche holds a Leverhulme Early Career
Fellowship at the London School of Economics
and Political Science. Her research interests are
in representation and migration with a focus on
western India.

Original credits from
the Brunei Gallery
exhibition, 2015.

225

CURATION
Edward Simpson

CONTRIBUTORS
F.G. Bailey,
George St Clair,
Surinder S. Jodhka,
Adrian Mayer,
Daniela Neri,
Tina Otten,
Tommaso Sbriccoli,
Edward Simpson,
Alice Tilche and
Smita Yadav.

DESIGN & WALL GRAPHICS
Madeline Herbert.

DESIGN INSPIRATION
Claudia Mayer.

TEXT DESIGN
Nicole Roughton.

PRINTING &
GRAPHICAL PRODUCTION
DPC Greenwich and
The Graphical Tree.

EDITING &
FILM PRODUCTION
Dakxin Bajrange and
William Elliott-Mills.

Copyright permission
for F.G. Bailey's *The
civility of indifference*
was kindly granted by the
Cornell University Press.

Copyright for Life
of Gandhi 1869-1948
(part 9), Call of the
villages, 1934-1938
lies with Gandhi
Films Foundation.

THANKS TO

Richard Axelby,
CAMP-Mumbai,
CSS-Surat,
John Bailey,
Hrudananda Barik,
Deepanjali Bisoi,
Jayadev Bisoi,
Mahendra Bisoi,
Sasi Bhusan Bisoi,
Upendra Bisoi,
Richard Black,
Jamie Cross,
David Cutts,
Purandhara Dehuri,
Lambadara Dehuri,
Aditya Dogra,
Jens Franz,
Chris Fuller,
John Hollingworth,
Patricia Jeffrey,
Balakrushna Kanhara,
Pabitra Kanhara,
Isabella Lepri,
Paula Levin,
Michael H.Lyon,
Bernice J.M Lyon,
Mrutyunjaya Mahapatro,
Phaguni Mallick,
Baladeba Mishra,
Kanhu Charan Mishra,
Madhusudan Mishra,
Nandikishore Mohapatra,
Trilochono Mishra,
Johnny Parry,
Alpesh Patel,
Chandrika Patel,
Pinakin Patel,
Rajesh Patel,
Ganesh Chandra Patro,
Adikanda Sahani,
Khirod Sahani,
Radhashyam Sahani,
Vesna Siljanovska,
Subir Sinha,
Sunny Suna,
Harald Tambs-Lyche,
Indira Varma,
Paul Webley,
and Zoe Williams.

Finally, thanks to the
residents, past and
present, of the villages
of Sundarana in Gujarat,
Jamgod in Madhya Pradesh
and Bisipada in Odisha.